A Career in Speech and Language Therapy

Jannet A Wright and Myra Kersner

Metacom Education
London

Published by Metacom Education
PO Box 48508, Hendon, London, NW4 4WP

http://metacomeducation.tripod.com

First published in Great Britain by Metacom Education 2004

Note: The rights of Jannet A Wright and Myra Kersner to be identified as the authors of this work has been asserted by them in accordance with the Copyright, Designs and Patents Act 1988.

Copyright © Jannet A Wright and Myra Kersner 2004

ISBN: 0-9547457-0-1

All rights reserved. No part of this publication may be reproduced, stored in a retrieval system or transmitted, in any form, or by any means, electronic, mechanical, photocopying, recording or otherwise, without the prior permission of the publisher.

Produced by Central Publishing Services • Royd Street • Offices • Milnsbridge • Huddersfield • HD3 4QY • www.centralpublishing.co.uk

Contents

List of Figures   i

Foreword   ii

Acknowledgements   iii

Abbreviations   iv

The Authors   vi

How to use this book   vi

**Introduction: A career in speech and language   1
therapy**

1   Frequently asked questions   2

Part I   Speech and language therapy as a career   11

2   Speech and language therapy   12

3   Human communication   14

4   Communication disorders   20

5   Ways of working   33

6   Where therapists work   45

7   What a therapist does   52

8   The skills and qualities needed as a student   68

9   The skills and qualities needed as a therapist   86

10   Is this career for you? How to find out more   93

Part II   Case studies – profiles of speech and language therapists at work in a variety of settings   97

11   Susan:
a paediatric specialist in a Child Development Centre   98

12   David:
a specialist working with adults in an acute hospital   105

13   Amita:
a paediatric therapist working in mainstream schools   111

14   Penny:
a specialist working with people who stammer   117

15   Andrew:
working in a special school   121

16   Moira:
a peripatetic therapist working in a rural area   126

17   Kirsty:
a newly qualified therapist in a split post   130

18   Sam:
working with people with learning disabilities   135

19   Charlotte:
a speech and language therapy manager   140

20   Angela: 145
     working in a school for deaf children

Part III   Applying for a speech and language   149
therapy course

21   How to set about becoming a speech and language   150
     therapist

22   Where can you train?   154

23   Entry requirements   158

24   Funding   161

25   Making initial contact   163

26   Skills, qualities and experience   164

27   Filling out the application form   167

28   Being interviewed   173

29   Selection   177

Part IV   Being a student   181

30   The student group   182

31   Studying and professional development   187

Part V   Now you are qualified...   193

32   Applying for a job   194

33   Life after qualification   197

Appendix   202

Further reading   203

Useful addresses   205

Index   207

List of Figures

Figure	1	The speech and language chain	17
Figure	2	Breakdown of your own communication	20
Figure	3	Your list of different types of communication problems	24
Figure	4	Communication problems	25
Figure	5	What you think a speech and language therapist does	52
Figure	6	What speech and language therapists are not	53
Figure	7	What speech and language therapists are	54
Figure	8	A speech and language therapy job description	55
Figure	9	The skills and knowledge required to understand speech and language	57
Figure	10	Brief summary of subject areas studied	58
Figure	11	Flow chart of the speech and language therapy process	60
Figure	12	The attractions of speech and language therapy as a career	68
Figure	13	Person specification – for a speech and language therapy student	71
Figure	14	Essential requirements to work as a speech and language therapist	86
Figure	15	University courses in the UK	154

Foreword

Many people take up careers without properly understanding what is involved. Consequently they find that their chosen field, selected on inadequate information, is not for them and try to change course mid-stream. That could have applied to speech and language therapy, until now. For the emergence of this book will shine a vivid light on a little understood profession.

It is a superb account of the complexities of the subject told with striking clarity. It is also a comprehensive guide to the profession. The book is packed with useful information and laced generously with good judgement. This is a fine practical guide to a fine profession.

Jannet Wright and Myra Kersner pose a question in the first sentence of their introduction:

'What can I read to find out more about speech and language therapy?'

In writing this splendid book they have given a comprehensive answer. People should read this book.

Rt. Hon. Lord Ashley of Stoke, C.H.
Former President
Royal College of Speech and Language Therapists

Acknowledgements

We would like to acknowledge the help and support of our speech and language therapy colleagues and friends by thanking the following people. We appreciate the time and effort taken to give us such helpful feedback.

Michael Clarke
Elizabeth Dean
Juliette Jamieson
Zeeba Kazi
Carolyn Letts
Clare Morris
Ann Parker
Christina Smith
Maggie Vance
Ray Wilkinson
Claire Withey
Louise Wright
Emma Winn

Abbreviations

AAC   Alternative and Augmentative Communication

Afasic   UK charity working with children with speech and language disabilities

ASLTIP   Association of Speech and Language Therapists in Independent Practice

BSL   British Sign Language

CV   Curriculum Vitae

CVA   Cerebro-vascular accident

ENT   Ear, Nose and Throat

EU   European Union

HPC   Health Professions Council

I CAN   A charity helping children with speech and language difficulties

IELTS   International English Language Testing System

LEA   Local Education Authority

LSA   Learning Support Assistant

MBA   Master's degree in Business Administration

Mencap   UK charity specialising in working with people with learning disabilities

NHS	National Health Service
PCT	Primary Care Trust
RCSLT	Royal College of Speech and Language Therapists
Scope	A disability organisation in the UK specialising in cerebral palsy
SENCo	Special Educational Needs Co-ordinator
SIG	Special Interest Group
UCAS	Universities and Colleges Admissions Service
VSO	Voluntary Service Overseas

The authors

Jannet Wright and Myra Kersner have both worked as speech and language therapists and have a range of clinical experience. For many years they have been involved in the education and training of speech and language therapy students at undergraduate and post-graduate level in the Department of Human Communication Science at University College London. There, Jannet Wright is the Departmental Admissions Tutor and Myra Kersner has been responsible for developing and running the Master's degree programme.

They combine extensive writing on aspects of speech and language therapy with their work as lecturers and tutors. They have each at different times supervised the Continuing Professional Development programme offered to qualified therapists by the department and have run many workshops and courses for therapists. In addition, they have both been extensively involved with the professional body, the Royal College of Speech and Language Therapists (RCSLT). In recognition of their work Myra Kersner has been awarded the Honours of the Royal College, and Jannet Wright a Fellowship of the Royal College.

Details about other publications by the authors are available on the website http://metacomeducation.tripod.com

How to use this book

This book is intended for a wide range of readers: anyone of school age considering their career, mature students looking for a new career path, or parents who may be investigating a career for their child.

There may, therefore, be some sections of the book that are more relevant to you than others and individual readers may find themselves dipping into different sections that are of particular interest and relevance to them. For those who are reading the book from cover to cover there may, of necessity, be some repetition, as some more important aspects are included in more than one section.

The book has been written from a UK perspective and applicants to universities outside of the UK will need to check on the requirements of the universities to which they wish to apply.

We hope that the contents page and the index will help you locate easily the details you require.

All acronyms used are explained in the *Abbreviations* section. Websites referred to in the text are given in full in *Useful Addresses*. The *Further Reading* section includes books that many speech and language therapy students have found useful.

Order forms are printable from the website if you wish to order further copies of this book.

Introduction:
A Career in Speech and Language Therapy

Chapter 1 Frequently asked questions

What can I read?

We are always being asked by potential students, 'What can I read to find out more about speech and language therapy?' As we have considerable experience writing successful textbooks for students as well as books on speech and language problems for parents and other professionals, we decided to write *A Career in Speech and Language Therapy* in the hope that it will answer that question for you. We hope the information in the following pages will help you to make an informed decision about your future career.

The book is aimed at anyone who is thinking about a career in speech and language therapy (which used to be known as speech therapy). It is suitable for school leavers and mature students interested in undergraduate study; it will also be of interest to those with a first degree who are not yet on a specific career path, or those wanting a change of career who are considering post-graduate study. In addition, it should be of interest to parents, teachers and careers advisors who may be guiding and helping others in their choice of career.

Is it an easy job?

We hope *A Career in Speech and Language Therapy* will offer insights into how to obtain an appropriate degree and into the professional role, showing how speech and language therapists work with people with communication problems, and eating, drinking and swallowing problems, in a variety of settings. But we hope it will do more than that. For speech and language therapists are among those highly trained and skilled professionals who manage to make their job look easy. We hope to show you some of its complexities.

2

As with any complex job, what makes it appear easy is the therapists' mastery of the required individual skills and knowledge, and their mastery of the ability to process their thoughts and actions simultaneously, at speed. Observers – and service users – only see the end result of this process, the therapists' actions. What they may not be aware of is how quickly therapists are able to access and process their knowledge in order to interpret the behaviour they are observing. For in order to be able to work effectively, therapists need to be able to think, observe and record almost at the same time as they are accessing the information and knowledge that will help them come to conclusions and make decisions.

We aim to show you the individual aspects of this process that speech and language therapists develop during their education and training; the process that enables them to become so proficient at their highly skilled jobs.

Throughout the following pages we will guide you through the complexities of the job of being a speech and language therapist so that by the end of the book you may understand why, if you decide this is the career for you, you will need to study hard.

What are the career prospects?

At the time of writing there continues to be a high demand for speech and language therapists and there are jobs available in a variety of settings within the NHS, in educational settings, in the private sector, and in the voluntary sector. Part-time as well as full-time work is often available.

All the courses referred to qualify you to practise as a speech and language therapist within the UK and it may be possible to work in some countries abroad.

Speech and language therapy is a profession where career breaks are not uncommon and there is support and supervision for those wanting to return to the profession.

Can I work abroad with the qualification?

This will depend on where you want to work, the language requirements of that country's professional body and whether there is reciprocal recognition between the professional bodies. For example, currently in the USA, Canada or Australia you would need to have a Master's degree and provide a transcript from your university of the hours studied in each aspect of the course in order for your application to be considered. In many countries you will be asked to sit additional examinations and you will often find that each state or province within a country will have its own additional regulations.

Do employers view the undergraduate and post-graduate students differently when they are first qualified?

No, there is no difference between the status of those completing a BSc or those completing an MSc in the UK. All newly graduating students are eligible to start at the same spine point on the pay scale and will be qualified to apply for the same jobs.

How easy is it to get a job?

Currently there is great demand for speech and language therapists throughout the country, although you may have to be flexible if you have a preference for a specific location or want to work with a specific client group.

Is speech and language therapy really a profession? I thought that was only medicine.

Yes, speech and language therapy is a profession in its own right and is considered to be one of the professions 'allied to medicine'. The courses are shorter than when studying for medicine but are none the less rigorous and include practical work experience so that on successful completion you are qualified for recommendation for registration on the national register.

All the therapists I've seen so far are women. Are there any male speech and language therapists?

Yes, quite a number but not as many as are needed if there is to be a balance in the profession. The professional body and the NHS confederations responsible for funding speech and language therapy students are working towards widening access, and the universities are also trying to encourage more men to apply for their speech and language therapy courses.

I come from a multi-cultural background and I speak another language. Will this be a help?

There are many people living in the UK for whom English is an additional language who need help from a speech and language therapist because they have a communication disorder, so it is a great advantage if therapists speak more than one language themselves. The profession needs representatives from as many different cultural groups as possible as people with communication difficulties come from a wide variety of backgrounds. The professional body and the NHS are working with the universities to widen access and encourage people from all ethnic and cultural backgrounds to consider speech and language therapy as a career.

If the NHS funds my course, will I have to guarantee to work for them for a certain number of years after I've qualified?

No. There is no obligation currently, although most speech and language therapy jobs in England and Wales are within the NHS, even those based in educational settings.

Should I learn a sign language?

You might want to learn British Sign Language (BSL) for your own interest. British Sign Language is the language of deaf people in the UK. However, there are different sign-based systems such as Paget Gorman Signed Speech and there are some signing systems based on BSL, such as Makaton, which you may come across if you work, for example, with people with learning disabilities. Sign language is not usually taught as part of a speech and language therapy degree course although you may find pre-knowledge useful in specific practical placements.

When would I start going on practical placement?

This varies according to each university. RCSLT stipulate that students should work on placement for a minimum number of hours and most courses exceed this number when their students attend a variety of day-release placements and short or long placement blocks. You may find more specific information on individual university departmental websites.

Can I choose my own research project?

A research project or dissertation is not a requirement on all speech and language therapy courses and you should check for details with the individual university.

I haven't got a science background. Will this go against me?

It is possible you may still be offered a place on some courses. However, if you have the opportunity to study science subjects at GCSE, AS or A level this will enhance your application and increase your options as several of the universities do require a science. A science subject will be helpful to you as there are many scientific aspects to speech and language therapy courses such as anatomy, physiology, acoustics and statistics. If you are a mature student and want to take an A level to provide evidence of recent study, you should check if the university of your choice has any subject preferences. Biology, or psychology are often preferred.

I have been to observe a therapist working with a young child and am wondering why I need a degree to play?

What may have seemed to you like 'play' was most likely a carefully structured and monitored assessment and therapy session. Don't forget that play is work for children. When children play therapists are able to observe and assess their behaviour and responses. This often gives vital clues about the nature of a child's problems and by interpreting their observations a therapist is often able to make decisions about what to do next.

As an analogy, championship ice-skaters make their athletic leaps look easy but, if you were to try jumping while spinning and twisting without falling over, you would realise that most highly skilled tasks are more difficult than they look.

What other professionals would I work with?

That would depend on the setting in which you were working. If you worked in schools you would work with teachers, assistants, special educational needs co-ordinators, educational psychologists and possibly social workers. In a clinical setting you may work with consultants, surgeons and other medical specialists, psychiatrists, psychologists, physiotherapists, occupational therapists, specialist nurses, dieticians... any professional who works in a hospital or clinic. If you work with people with learning disabilities your team may also include key workers, instructors, social workers and residential staff.

Can I make a lot of money by becoming a speech and language therapist?

The salaries have greatly improved over the years and nowadays there are a variety of career opportunities available. Current salary scales are given on the RCSLT website.

Can I do anything else with the qualification if I change my mind and don't want to practise as a speech and language therapist after graduation?

If you have obtained a good class of degree you may wish to study further or to become a researcher. After gaining some clinical experience you may wish to work in one of the university departments and become part of the education and training system for future speech and language therapists. If you would prefer a complete change of career, it may be possible to work, for example, in some other aspect of communication. Or, for example, some graduates have become teachers, or moved into management or human resources. But the majority of graduates find their work so rewarding they prefer to practise as a speech and language therapist.

What if I want to take a career break after I have worked for a while?

Speech and language therapy is a profession where career breaks are not uncommon and there are many opportunities for you to refresh your knowledge and skills when you return.

You will find more detailed answers to these questions and to any other questions you may have in the following pages of this book.

Part I
Speech and Language Therapy as a Career

Chapter 2 Speech and language therapy

Speech and language therapy is an all-graduate profession. Therapists are currently trained at one of sixteen institutions throughout the UK and there are an additional four courses in the Republic of Ireland. In order to practise as a speech and language therapist in the UK you need to be registered with The Health Professions Council (HPC) the regulatory body for health professionals in the UK. HPC protect the title 'speech and language therapist' by law so that you cannot call yourself a speech and language therapist unless you are registered to practise by the Council.

Working as a speech and language therapist

Speech and language therapists are concerned with human communication, its development in young children – that begins at birth and continues throughout childhood and adolescence – and its breakdown, which may occur in people of all ages. The majority of therapists are employed by the NHS, working in hospitals and health centres, and many work in schools.

Therapists work with people whose speech and language has never developed. They also work with those who once spoke but have since lost their ability to use spoken language, perhaps through a head injury or a cerebro-vascular accident (CVA), more commonly referred to as a stroke. They work not only to improve the impaired speech, language and communication skills of those who are keen to communicate but they also work with people who cannot speak at all, and sometimes with those who don't even know how to communicate in any way. They are also concerned with people who have eating, drinking and swallowing difficulties and these may occur at any age for a variety of reasons.

Speech and language therapists are not voice coaches or elocution teachers who may help people improve their pronunciation, neither are they linguists. But, if you want to work with a variety of different people with a range of different communication problems, speech and language therapy may be the career for you.

Terms used

The difficulties people have are often referred to as 'problems', 'difficulties', 'impairments' or sometimes more specifically as 'disorders'. In this book all these terms will be used interchangeably.

In order to understand the difficulties that can occur with communication it is necessary to be aware how people typically communicate.

Chapter 3 Human communication

Human communication is about sending and receiving messages. We generally think of it in social terms, such as people talking together, writing emails or letters, sending text messages, or using sign language to communicate with each other. Such communication involves the development of language, that is, an agreed and accepted set of symbols that help us classify and order our world.

For most forms of human communication we express our language by developing the ability to speak and to write. Some people, such as deaf people, express themselves through sign language and this will often be their first language. Or, there are some who, for physical, cognitive (intellectual) or even psychological reasons, are unable to develop any of these skills. They may learn to use some alternative form of expression such as pointing to printed pictures, pointing to written words or to special symbols. In some instances technical and computerised aids may be needed instead of speech and writing.

Non-verbal communication

We can also communicate without speech or language. For instance, babies usually cry to indicate they need food or a nappy change. A mother then often uses soothing noises, not necessarily words, to help calm the baby, at least temporarily. Eventually, if all is well, the baby will indicate, 'I'm all right now', by making cooing or gurgling noises.

We also use 'body language' to communicate. If someone waves eagerly and smiles at you on first sighting, you will probably be pleased to meet them knowing they are pleased to see you. If, on the other hand, someone stands close to you and wags their finger at you, you don't need words to tell you they are annoyed.

Facial expressions, eye contact, stance, distance, and

gestures are all forms of body language that we use to express how we feel as well as to underline and enhance spoken language, or signed language.

Speech and language development

Young children normally acquire speech and language as they develop physically, intellectually and emotionally. First they show an interest in communication using sounds to express their feelings, and responding to the sounds of others as described above. This indicates that they are beginning to understand the rudiments of conversational turn-taking. Then they begin to understand and respond appropriately to spoken language. Gradually they will attempt to speak meaningful words themselves.

Single words like 'Daddy' will eventually be expanded into short phrases like 'Daddy work', then into simple sentences such as 'Daddy goes to work' and eventually into complex speech such as, 'I can't wait for Daddy to come home from work 'cos he's promised to bring me a present'.

For further information see *How to Manage Communication Problems in Young Children* (see *Further Reading*).

The speech and language chain

The way people talk to each other has been described as a 'communication chain' or a 'speech and language chain' because it involves a cycle of:

producing a message → *sending a message* →
receiving a message →

This pattern can be broken down to its basic components. We can then analyse a simple conversation between two people who have no problems with their communication, and we can consider the skills required in order for them to conduct that conversation.

Figure 1 The speech and language chain

What happens in the conversation	The skills needed to be able to do this
❑ First speaker thinks of, produces and transmits a message of meaningful words.	❑ The mental ability to initiate the thought. ❑ The development of language so the speaker has the words to express that thought – a language that is common to the speaker and the listener. ❑ The physical ability to speak those specific words out loud. ❑ The ability of the speaker to monitor that what was said is what was intended. ❑ Physical ability to include non-verbal messages such as gestures, facial expression and eye contact.
❑ Second speaker receives and processes the message. ❑ The second speaker therefore becomes the first listener.	❑ The ability to concentrate and attend to the words of the first speaker. ❑ Visual ability to see the non-verbal messages. ❑ Acuity of hearing to receive the spoken message accurately. ❑ Visual and mental ability to interpret the non-verbal messages. ❑ The knowledge of a common language with the speaker so that the received message can be understood ❑ The mental ability to process the meaning of the words. ❑ The mental ability to interpret the message.
❑ The first listener then becomes the second speaker. ❑ The second speaker responds to first speaker's words.	❑ The mental ability to think of an appropriate response. ❑ The linguistic ability to find the words for that response. ❑ The physical ability to speak the response out loud. ❑ Ability to monitor that what has been said is what was intended. ❑ Physical ability to include non-verbal messages.

The first speaker then becomes the second listener, hearing, interpreting and responding to the second speaker's words and so the chain continues until the conversation is terminated by one or the other of the speakers usually by mutual, albeit tacit, agreement.

Such tacit agreement highlights another important aspect of social conversation. Human communication can only work effectively if both speakers understand and comply not only with the grammatical, linguistic rules of their common language but also with the commonly accepted pragmatic rules of social interaction.

Pragmatics – rules of interaction

In order to be able to converse successfully, both speakers need to understand some of the basic rules of communication that help them to synchronise their communication with others. For example, in many face-to-face conversations between acquaintances:

- The speakers take turns.
- The second speaker does not begin before the first speaker has finished most of what they are going to say.
- Each speaker listens to the other and normally responds with words related to the other speaker's words.
- The speaker who changes topic will normally introduce this change in some way.
- There will usually be some eye contact between the speakers.
- Often non-verbal feedback will be given by the listener, such as nodding, or vocalising such as 'mmm'.
- The speakers will normally maintain some physical distance between them.
- The level of voice will normally be appropriate for the surroundings so that they are not shouting unnecessarily.

All this might seem like common sense, but these rules have to be learned. There will be some instances when the rules are not applied because someone may choose not to obey the rules. Or, it may be that they have not been able to learn the rules; or they may have learned the rules but for some reason are no longer able to apply them. But most 'normal' conversations, when there is no evidence of communication problems in either of the speakers, follow a predictable 'ping-pong' pattern.

Chapter 4 Communication disorders

Sometimes, however, some aspect of communication can fail to develop, or it can break down after speech and language has already been acquired which can happen to anybody at any age. Problems can occur at any level of the speech and language chain. Sometimes breakdown may take place over a long period of time, or it may happen quite suddenly. Imagine how frightening it would be to wake up and suddenly find it's impossible to speak or, in some cases, even to understand what others are saying, an experience described by many people before they realised they had had a stroke.

We all experience problems with our communication at some time in our lives, although not every kind of communication breakdown requires the help of a speech and language therapist.

When communication breaks down

Can you think of three occasions when you experienced problems with your own communication? Although, of course, there may have been many more. You might want to write them down in Figure 2 below.

Figure 2 Breakdown of your own communication

Your examples might have included:
- ➤ The time you were on holiday in a country where you didn't speak the language.
- ➤ Meeting someone who spoke with a strong accent that you found hard to understand.
- ➤ Using your mobile phone in a noisy environment and you couldn't hear what the other person was saying.
- ➤ Talking to someone much younger than yourself and you didn't understand their fashionable idioms.
- ➤ Having had a numbing injection at the dentist so that you couldn't move your mouth to speak comfortably.

You will notice that some of these examples involved you as the 'listener' in the exchange; some involved you as the 'speaker', while some involved a difficult environment. All resulted in a problem with the communication, but each would require a different type of solution in order to improve it.

For example, as a listener you would probably get used to the speaker's accent if you persevered and would soon be able to understand them. Or, you might ask for clarification of certain words or expressions. If you are in a noisy environment you may simply need to move to a quieter place.

Associated feelings

Think about how you – and the person with whom you were trying to communicate – felt on any of these occasions when communication broke down.

You will probably have answered 'frustrated' or 'embarrassed'.

Think about how you feel, and what you do, when you are in a restaurant but do not understand what a waiter, for whom English is not a first language, is saying when trying to name a specific dish. Or, when he does not understand you, and without the visual prompt of the menu you are not able to make your own choices known.

But in all of these examples the conditions are mostly temporary and given time – or possibly by you taking a specific action – communication soon gets back to normal. These are not the kind of communication problems dealt with by a speech and language therapist.

Examples of communication difficulties

Your examples of communication breakdown might, however, have included:

> Trying to communicate with someone, face-to-face or on the phone, who was losing their hearing.
> Talking to someone who had had a road traffic accident or a stroke, who did not seem able to understand you.
> Talking to a child with a physical difficulty whose speech was very unclear.

These examples of communication difficulties are more serious and in these instances you would no doubt feel more than frustrated when you were trying to communicate. You might feel anxious if you could not understand the speaker whose speech is impaired. So, imagine how frightened and anxious they would feel if they were suddenly not able to express themselves through speech. They might also feel frightened if they found that suddenly they were not able to understand any of the words spoken to them.

Sometimes, people who are able to understand but are not able to speak clearly for some reason, say that they feel angry when others speak to them with what has become known as a *'does he take sugar'* approach. That is, instead of being addressed directly, they are spoken to as if they are stupid – or not there – and maybe someone else is asked to respond on their behalf. People who have 'normal' intelligence but who, because of their physical difficulties, are not able to speak and are sitting in wheelchairs, perhaps relying on pointing to pictures or symbols to express themselves, often complain of such treatment.

These more serious types of communication difficulties are the kinds that are unlikely to improve without some specific help and this would include working with a speech and language therapist.

Some facts and figures about communication problems

It is estimated that currently in the UK there are approximately 2.5 million people with some form of communication disorder, with about 32% of them having an extremely severe level of difficulty which would probably require the help of a speech and language therapist. Five per cent of children entering school have some form of speech and language difficulty and 30% of people who have had a stroke have communication difficulties that do not automatically clear up.

You might know someone who has had a communication problem that is not easily resolved. It may be a child who is not developing speech or language normally which may be affecting their overall development and their ability to manage in school. Or, it may be an adult who has had an illness or an accident causing them to lose some of their communicative skills and affecting all aspects of their life at home and at work.

Communication problems

How many different types of communication problems or communication disorders can you think of? You might want to write them down in Figure 3 below.

Figure 3 Your list of different types of communication problems

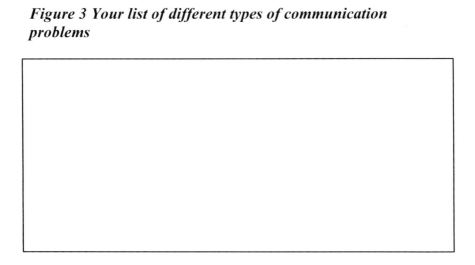

The type of communication problems speech and language therapists deal with will vary. Some communication problems are related to other areas of difficulty such as when people have chronic physical problems like cerebral palsy, or cognitive problems such as some level of learning disability. Some may be associated with long-term, progressive neurological conditions such as Motor Neurone Disease, Parkinson's Disease or Multiple Sclerosis. Or, they may be associated with 'sudden onset' problems such as a stroke or a head injury resulting from a road traffic accident.

There are other kinds of communication problems that occur in people who have no other kind of difficulties. These might include stammering, specific speech and language disorders, or voice disorders.

Did you include any of these in your list?

The kinds of problems that would usually require the help of a speech and language therapist are given below.

Figure 4 Communication problems

Communication problems that may arise in relation to, or in association with, other difficulties or diseases	Communication problems that are not necessarily related to or associated with other problems
People with: Cerebral palsy Learning disabilities Neurological conditions Strokes Autistic spectrum disorders including Asperger's Syndrome Severe emotional/behavioural problems Psychiatric problems Head injuries Alzheimer's Disease Dementia Medical conditions such as cancer of the head and neck resulting in laryngectomy (removal of the larynx or vocal cords), or glossectomy (removal of the tongue)	Language delay and disorder Cleft palate Stammering Hearing loss Voice problems Specific speech and language problems Comprehension difficulties Interaction – social skills problems Expressive difficulties (finding the words) Pragmatic problems (using language appropriately)

Each type of communication difficulty will follow a different pattern and there will be different levels of severity. Some beginning in childhood may disappear as the child develops, while others may continue into adulthood. For example, a problem such as 'language delay' that occurs in childhood may disappear with a therapist's help as the child grows and develops.

On the other hand, a problem associated with autistic spectrum disorder may be more severe and although, with help, communication may improve as the child grows older, some level of difficulty will often remain.

Problems such as those associated with progressive conditions like Parkinson's Disease, or Motor Neurone Disease will only occur in adults. These will never be 'cured' as the disease progresses, although a therapist may provide much support and help to the client in maintaining their communication skills.

Eating, drinking and swallowing difficulties (dysphagia)

Speech and language therapists also work with people who have eating, drinking and swallowing difficulties. The lips, tongue, hard and soft palate and the throat that are involved in producing the sounds needed for speech also play a vital role in the swallowing action when eating and drinking.

Feeding difficulties may occur in young babies who are unable to suck or swallow easily, such as in some children with a cleft lip and palate, but many of these difficulties may be resolved in childhood.

Eating, drinking and swallowing difficulties may also be associated with many of the conditions which give rise to communication problems such as in children with cerebral palsy or in children who have intellectual difficulties (i.e. cognitive difficulties), for example, those with severe learning disabilities. When such problems occur in young children they may persist and continue into adulthood.

As with communication problems, eating, drinking and swallowing problems may also be 'acquired' after normal patterns have been established. This may occur when people have had a stroke, contracted a progressive disease or as the result of an accident.

Eating and drinking are usually considered to be social activities so when people have difficulties with swallowing, this may often have implications for their social lives. For example, they may be unable, or unwilling, to eat or drink in public.

Different kinds of communication problems

Each of the communication disorders mentioned above will result in different types of problems and will affect the person's ability to communicate in different ways. The nature of the problem and the effects it has on the individual concerned will affect the approach the speech and language therapist has to take in order to help them.

Speech problems

Sometimes people have unclear speech and listeners are not always able to understand them. For example, some children do not master the ability to make all the sounds in a language and their speech could be almost unintelligible. Or, a problem such as a cleft lip and palate might make a child's speech unclear. Similarly a person of any age who has a voice problem will find that it is their speech, not their ability to understand and manipulate language that is affected. Only if there are additional problems such as a hearing loss might there be additional difficulties with developing or understanding language.

Language problems

Language problems can occur at any age. For example, children such as those with learning disabilities may be good communicators non-verbally and may even have clear speech, but it is likely that the language that they understand and use will be limited to some degree. They may have a variety of problems when trying to express themselves such as a limited vocabulary, difficulty using correct syntax or grammar, or difficulty finding the appropriate word.

Another example would be a five-year-old child who would normally be expected to say a sentence such as, 'I'm going into the garden.' A five year old with syntax problems, however, might say, 'Me go garden,' an expression more commonly found in a two to three-year-old child.

A man who has difficulties finding words as the result of a stroke might look at the back page of a newspaper in response to the question, 'What is happening in the goalmouth?' and say something like, 'That one, there, there....' They may be the only words he can find to describe the picture, when what he should have said was something like, 'He's scoring a goal.'

Pragmatic problems

Sometimes a person may have competent speech skills and adequate language but the difficulties lie in their ability to use speech and language appropriately in social settings. These pragmatic difficulties may result in what are referred to as 'social skills' problems, where the person affected may not know how to take turns in a conversation, how to begin a conversation appropriately, how to end one, or how to respond appropriately to specific questions.

For example, sometimes children who have some degree of autistic spectrum disorder, but who do not have associated learning disabilities, may have perfect-sounding speech and language. Their problems are often associated with the ability to communicate appropriately in a more general sense. For instance, they may not make eye contact, or they may speak out of turn, or speak over the other person, not taking their conversational 'turn' and without listening to what is being said.

Or, they may interpret what is being said to them literally even when someone is using an idiom. For example, on hearing 'pull your socks up' when used in the sense of 'get moving and get on with it' such a child might bend down and pull his socks up.

Another example of using language inappropriately might be a child with severe learning disabilities who might approach you saying, 'Hello, I like your dress.' This sounds fine until you realise they are saying the same thing to every woman – and man – that they meet, and saying it every time they meet them.

Speech, language and communication problems

More often people experience a combination of speech, language and communication problems which often makes diagnosis difficult as it is not always easy for the speech and language therapist to tease out the different aspects of the problem.

This may happen for example, when someone has had a stroke. This may affect any aspect of their speech and language as well as their overall ability to communicate. Non-verbal aspects such as eye contact or gesturing may have become difficult.

Or, for example, some children with cerebral palsy may have problems with speech and with aspects of non-verbal communication because of the physical nature of their condition, although they will not necessarily have problems understanding language.

Associated factors

How people are affected by their communication difficulty will also depend on several other factors. For example, it will depend on their general health and their current situation such as their support system of family and friends. It will also depend on whether the problem has been with them since birth or has been acquired later. It will depend on their age, and whether there is the added complication of other physical or sensory problems such as hearing or visual difficulties.

'Developmental' vs. 'acquired'

When children fail to make progress at the normally expected rate or their skills fail to develop in the normally expected sequence they are said to have 'developmental problems'. If speech and language skills do not develop at the appropriate stage they are said to have 'developmental' speech and language problems.

If speech and/or language is lost, for example, as the result of an accident or illness, this is said to be an 'acquired' speech and language problem.

Whether a speech and language problem is considered to be a 'developmental' or an 'acquired' problem will greatly affect how it is managed by the speech and language therapist and any other professionals involved in therapy.

Age of the client

The age at which the person was affected initially by the problem, as well as their current age, will often influence how a problem evolves and the approaches to therapy taken by the speech and language therapist. For example, the age of a client affects the resources available, as there is a divide in the NHS between child and adult services.

When working with children there will be educational issues to consider, such as the need to work with teachers to ensure access to the curriculum. With adults there will be issues of employment and returning to work to be considered.

The age of the client will also have an impact on who else may be involved in the therapy and the degree of that involvement. For example, parents will be expected to be closely involved in any therapy offered to young children prior to school entry. Similarly, the partners, relatives or friends of adult clients will often be involved in their therapy.

Physical and sensory difficulties

Additional physical problems, such as following a stroke when a person's mobility is often reduced, or where a person has a sensory loss such as a hearing loss, will also add to the management decisions the speech and language therapist has to make regarding therapy.

'Clients' or 'patients'

Before discussing more details of the therapist's work it would be helpful to clarify some terminology regarding the people with whom a therapist works.

Some therapists refer to the people they work with as 'clients', some refer to 'patients'. Is there a difference? In hospitals and in some Child Development Centres, outpatient clinics and even some health centres, therapists usually refer to their 'patients' because the people they work with are patients within that medical setting.

However, many speech and language therapists work in non-medical settings, in education settings where they work with children or students such as in schools, units and nurseries. Or they may work in day centres that are run by social services. Here the service users are not 'ill' and it is not appropriate to refer to them as 'patients'. In such instances it is more usual to refer to the people they work with as 'clients' or sometimes as 'service users'.

A holistic view

Speech and language therapists do not deal with a speech and/or a language problem or a swallowing difficulty in isolation. They have to take a holistic view of each person in their care, considering the whole person in relation to their family, friends, school or job and social setting. They have to help that person develop their communication skills so that they can interact as comfortably as possible in their own social environment.

With children this may mean helping them to access the curriculum and to manage themselves so that they can fulfil their potential at school; with teenagers it may mean helping them to cope with the transition from school to work; with adults it may mean helping them return to work, or to adjust to a different lifestyle if they can no longer work.

Sometimes therapists, as part of their work, may be called on to help people and their relatives adjust to the changes which have occurred in their lives as a result of the communication or swallowing problems, or to help parents as they struggle to come to terms with having a child who has difficulties.

This means that speech and language therapists are required to carry out many different types of tasks and to take on many different roles.

Chapter 5 Ways of working

One of the things qualified therapists often say they enjoy most about the job is the variety of different aspects there are to the work. Part of this variety relates to the fact that therapists work in different ways and are required to take on different roles. Sometimes this may mean that an individual job requires you to take on a role that is different from one normally associated with therapy. Or it may mean that you take on many different roles as you do a range of tasks during the course of one day. The number and type of roles will depend on the setting and the client group.

Taking on 'roles' does not mean you stop being 'you'. It means that you have to work in a variety of specific and different ways with the clients and their families because of their specific needs.

The professional role

Whichever way you work you will always need to 'be professional' although what this means is often difficult to define. 'Professionalism' is the 'secret ingredient' that enables your clients and their relatives, friends or carers to have confidence in your competence. It is your attitude, the way you behave, the way you demonstrate your skills and the public face you present that shows others that you have confidence in your own abilities. This helps to reassure them that you are capable of doing the job.

In practical terms it may sometimes mean that you present to the world a confident and 'professional' outside face while not feeling wonderful inside. It doesn't matter that you had a row at home that morning and deep down are still brooding about it; it doesn't matter that the patient's plight reminds you of your own grandmother and you find it distressing. In the professional setting you need to hide your own feelings and concerns about yourself in order to show your genuine warmth and empathy through your 'professional' face to your clients and their carers.

Some therapists find some roles more comfortable to perform than others and the roles required in a specific post may help you to decide on your choice of job.

The varieties of roles taken on by speech and language therapists generally are described below.

A therapeutic role

It may sound obvious to say that therapists carry out therapy, but often using direct therapy with clients may only be a small part of a therapist's daily routine. There is also a frequent assumption that therapy is always carried out on a one-to-one basis. But this is not the case and you may be disappointed if wanting to work with people individually was your major motivation for becoming a speech and language therapist.

Many therapists work with groups of adults or children and these groups might be small or large. For example, running a stroke club might involve working with a large number of people including organising the work of the volunteers. Or, if you are working in a special unit attached to a school, this could involve you in working with the whole class.

The way therapists work when carrying out therapy will vary too. Normally they need to use different approaches to help clients improve and this may depend on whether it is speech or language that is the main focus of the therapy.

The teaching role within therapy

People do not learn language skills merely by imitating words and therapists rarely ask clients to copy words they have just said in order to help them develop their language. The teaching role in this instance may involve therapists modelling a word, a phrase or a sentence so that the client can hear the appropriate form.

However, there are times when the client may need to imitate the therapist's model, for example, if working on speech sounds as this may help those who are having difficulty matching their speech to the target sounds. This will normally be done in association with other activities such as developing finely-tuned listening skills and helping the client to distinguish between acceptable and non-acceptable sounds.

Teaching a technique

Sometimes the therapist may need to teach clients a particular technique or approach. For example, if working with clients who stammer, the therapist may teach them how to slow their speech down or to break up their speech patterns rhythmically in order to reduce the frequency and severity of the stammer. Or, when working with people with voice problems, it may be necessary to teach them different breathing patterns that will help to improve their voice.

Another example would be if the therapist were teaching listening, for instance, with a boy of six who still says 'tea' instead of 'key'. The therapist will help him to produce the appropriate sound maybe using some imitation. In addition to helping him say the initial 'k' sound at the beginning of the word, the therapist will also try to help him hear the difference between the 't' and 'k' sounds. The therapist will help the child distinguish the sounds, not only when s/he makes them, but also when the child himself is saying them – a much more difficult thing to do.

When working with children who have difficulties with syntax, or grammar, the therapist may teach them how and when to use a specific grammatical form such as prepositions. This does not mean they will try to teach every preposition. Rather the therapist will teach the concept for example of 'in', 'on', and 'under', and link the concept to the word so that the child can begin to understand the contexts in which such words are used.

The facilitating role within therapy

At other times, therapists may take more of a facilitating role when working directly with the clients, particularly with adults. This means they will try to find ways of encouraging and helping them to use some aspect of their speech and language they are struggling with.

Often what clients need are more opportunities to use the words they have. So, for example, someone who has had a stroke may be prompted with cues and clues so that they may access their limited vocabulary.

Or, with a child who is using a limited amount of expressive language, the therapist may carefully construct play sessions in which the child is encouraged to talk while playing, expressing thoughts about what they are doing. They are not necessarily being asked to interact with or talk to the therapist. They are being encouraged to give their own running commentary on their play so that the therapist is 'facilitating' the child's use of language.

The assessment role

A large part of a therapist's role is carrying out assessments so that they can make decisions about what the problems are, and decide how to manage them and how to proceed. Speech and language therapy assessment is often continued over several sessions.

Assessing communication

Communication assessment in speech and language therapy is usually considered to be 'non-invasive', usually involving minimal physical contact. When speech is the main problem the therapist will normally need to do an oral examination but most of this can be done by observation, for example, of the tongue movements, or by looking at the movement of the soft palate at the back of the mouth with the aid of a pencil torch. Only in specific cases, such as when working with people with voice problems, might it be necessary to use specialised instruments to measure aspects of breathing and vocalisation.

Much assessment is done by observation of a client's behaviour in specific contexts, such as observing children playing in a structured setting, or by watching and listening to an adult client talking to their relatives.

Therapists will also record the client's responses during structured activities or their answers to questions about general pictures. In many instances the therapist will carry out an assessment from specifically published tests which may be standardised on a specific population. Then the therapist will make notes or record the client's responses on printed test forms, and sometimes will make an audio- or video-recording that can be transcribed later.

If English is an additional language for a child, and particularly if the parents or relatives do not speak English, it is not always easy to decide whether, for example, that child needs more opportunities to learn English or whether there is an underlying problem with the child's ability to learn any language.

Conversely, if an adult who has had a stroke has learned English as an additional language, it is not uncommon for much of their English to be forgotten following the stroke and for that person to revert to their first language. Then it may be necessary for the speech and language therapist to work through a co-worker, someone who is a fluent speaker of the client's first language who is not a speech and language therapist but who has had specific training.

Assessing eating, drinking and swallowing problems

Naturally, assessment of swallowing problems is more 'invasive' and will involve physical contact. Here the therapist is looking at the client's ability to swallow, the likelihood of choking if continuing to eat solid foods and their ability to deal with foods of different textures and consistency. They will also look at the possibility of the client inhaling food into the lungs as this can be dangerous. Decisions need to be made following assessment about whether surgical procedures or other arrangements such as nasal feeding, or drip feeding need to be considered and the speech and language therapist will then work with other members of the multi-disciplinary team.

Team working and collaboration

Most therapists will be part of a professional team, working closely with colleagues from other professions or with other speech and language therapists. This may be in schools, where therapists will have to work closely with teachers, learning support assistants (LSAs), educational psychologists, and special educational needs co-ordinators (SENCos). Or it may be in a hospital or clinical setting where the team might consist of doctors, nurses, physiotherapists, occupational therapists and social workers.

Speech and language therapists will also be part of teams working with people with learning disabilities which would include support workers, social workers and residential carers. The speech and language therapist may be the leader of the team or may be the key worker, taking the lead regarding a particular client.

Whether in the role of team leader or team member you will need to learn how to work closely with colleagues: knowing how to negotiate, when to stand firm and when to compromise. You will need to know when to be assertive, and how to put across your point of view so that others are willing to listen and support you in order to ensure that you are working together for the benefit of the client.

Working together helps you take a holistic approach to clients as discussed above. In order for you to help them fit into their social environment you need to look at all aspects of the clients' difficulties not just their speech and language in isolation.

Counselling role

Speech and language therapists are often called upon to use counselling skills, listening and supporting clients and their families. This might be when helping distressed parents understand the implications of having a communication disordered child, or helping relatives and carers adjust to the changes brought about in their lives when their relative's communication or their eating patterns are affected by a stroke or a progressive disease. However, speech and language therapists are not trained counsellors unless they have undertaken additional, specific training.

The training role

Often, instead of working directly with clients, therapists will work indirectly through other people. This usually means that they will work on raising the awareness of others about communication problems and train them to carry out specific therapy tasks, or even some aspects of assessment.

This can help the therapist to work more effectively as the time available for working with clients individually is often limited. Also, relatives or other team members such as residential workers normally spend much of the day with the clients so that any therapy they are able to carry out will be in surroundings that are familiar and natural for the client. The work will, therefore, be more meaningful and there will be more possibility of generalising the therapy into their everyday lives. For example, it is one thing working on naming cutlery and setting a table in a clinic but it will be far more meaningful if the skills are learned within the client's own home in preparation for a real meal.

Working with people with learning disabilities

Working through others is often a common approach, for example, when working with people with learning disabilities, particularly if they live in a hostel or a residential home. Initially, the therapist will usually work with the clients making careful observations as well as gathering information from support workers, social workers, the residential staff and all other helpers who see the clients on a regular basis and usually know the clients best.

The therapist, staff and clients will then work together to plan and devise speech and language therapy programmes. Once a programme is agreed and has begun to be implemented, the therapist will not necessarily continue to work directly with the client but will ensure that the team members are able to continue working on the programmes. The therapist will work with the staff regularly monitoring the clients' progress.

Working in residential settings

Therapists may also work with clients and staff in residential or nursing homes for elderly people, particularly if they are responsible for a number of such centres and have a large number of clients on their caseload.

Working in nurseries

Paediatric therapists are often responsible for several nurseries within their area and would find it impossible to work with every child individually who may need help. Often, therefore, it is more effective if the therapist works with the help of the staff who see the children on a more regular basis. The therapist can train the staff, for example, so that they are able to carry out specific work such as enhancing the children's language as part of their normal activities. Thus, within a class, the teacher, or assistant, may be able to work on language generally with children who may be 'at risk' and may often be able to prevent more serious difficulties from arising. If the staff are also shown how to recognise specific areas of difficulty, they can refer children who may have more complex problems to the therapist who may be able to work with them individually or in a small group.

Working with parents

Therapists work closely with parents of young children and this can prove to be beneficial in different ways. If the parents are able to become involved with the session and see how the therapist works with their child this then provides a model for them to continue working with their child at home.

Such a model also provides an opportunity for the therapist to observe the children interacting with their parents. The therapist can see how they talk together and sometimes how they play together. If the therapist feels it would be helpful, s/he may then decide to use a specially devised 'parent-child interaction programme', using a video to help the parents observe and monitor the ways in which they interact with their children.

It is not always easy for parents of children with communication problems to know how best to help and video work has proved useful in many instances when working with parents as it enables them to observe their own interactions and communication style. The therapist then has an opportunity to suggest specific ways for possible change that might prove beneficial to the child.

Working in this way is not to suggest that the parents were doing anything wrong or that they were in any way causing the children's problems and it is important to reinforce this to the parents. However, it can be helpful for many young children who have difficulty in communicating if their parents are able to modify their interaction patterns and in many instances the changes have been found to have a beneficial effect on children's language development.

Working with relatives

Similarly when working with adult clients it may be helpful to work with their relatives and sometimes it may be more helpful to suggest ways in which the relatives could modify their communication with the client rather than trying to change the client's communication skills.

For example, with a man who has had a stroke. His understanding may be greatly improved if his relatives slow their own speech, or highlight key words by repeating them or always putting them first in a sentence. His relatives could be encouraged to give him more time when he is trying to speak or to encourage him to try other ways of communicating such as using more gestures or writing down the key words.

Dysphagia training

When working with people with swallowing problems it may be possible to train other members of staff, such as nurses or assistants, to carry out some of the feeding techniques, or to work with relatives. Some of the training may be related to specific aspects of assessment as well as the management of people with swallowing problems.

It may be helpful to use anatomical models to demonstrate the process of eating and drinking. It might also be important to demonstrate sensitive handling of patients who are having swallowing difficulties as well as considering the preparation and consistency of food that is most appropriate for the individual client.

The role of advocate

Sometimes people with learning disabilities need responsible adults to act as advocates, enabling them to stand up for their rights and this too may part of be a speech and language therapist's role.

The administrative role

Speech and language therapists have much administrative work to complete as well as working with clients. The large amount of paper work involved in any therapy job, however, is one of the areas that newly qualified therapists often express surprise about, in spite of the many experiences they may have had during their practical work on placement as a student.

Therapists rarely have access to a secretary but they are required to keep their notes and records up-to-date and usually have to type up their own reports. In some settings they make their own appointments, book transport for the clients and answer all telephone calls coming into the speech and language therapy clinic. Speech and language therapists' employers will normally require them to keep some form of patients' statistical records and, in addition, they will need to keep a diary accounting for all of their work time not just client-contact time.

Time management

One of the other aspects therapists say they enjoy about their work is having autonomy and being able to manage their own time. This may be more constrained in a first job, where you will normally be more closely supervised, but generally most therapists are quickly made responsible for managing their own caseload and designing their own timetable.

Of course this is governed by the professional guidelines and expectations stipulated by the RCSLT in *Communicating Quality* 2 (RCSLT, 1996) or may be stipulated by an individual Trust's policy. These will include guidelines such as the length of time by which patients must be seen or they may affect the age parameters of children seen or how many sessions can be offered to clients within each 'episode of care'. For example, in some hospitals you may only be able to see a stroke patient for a prescribed number of sessions in the outpatients' department; or with pre-school children you may only be able to see them for a specific number of weekly sessions at a time before having a review.

There may also be targets set within a service for how many clients you should see over a given period of time and you will be responsible for managing your working day within these parameters.

Chapter 6 Where therapists work

Most speech and language therapists in the UK are employed within the NHS working in either the children's or adults' services, although there are opportunities for those who wish to work in independent, private practice. Therapists work in a wide variety of different settings and those employed within one Trust or one authority may work across a range of locations as part of their job. This provides the opportunity to work with many different professionals.

One of the advantages of speech and language therapy as a career is that it offers considerable flexibility and so, for example, therapists are often able to change their working hours. Part-time work is often available and accommodation can usually be made for those who want to take a career break.

Most therapists within the NHS work with children and these services may be educationally based, that is, offered within schools, or they may be based within the health service in a hospital or health centre. Adult services are more commonly hospital based. Therapists working with adults may, therefore, work in an acute service within a hospital where, for example, they would see people immediately after they had had a stroke or an accident. Some therapists may be part of a rehabilitation service linked to a specific rehabilitation unit or an outpatients' department. They will work with patients who have passed the acute phase and are ready for returning home.

How the therapist works in any particular setting will depend on how the individual service is organised.

Different ways of delivering the service

There are many different ways in which speech and language therapy services are organised and delivered and there is a huge variation across the country. This will often depend on the resources available, such as how many therapists there are *per capita* of the communication-disordered population within a region, local authority or Primary Care Trust. No one way has proved to be more effective than any other.

Therapy managers and organisers of the services – who will not necessarily be speech and language therapists – will use their resources in different ways. For example, some therapists will be expected to work all week in one place, while others will be peripatetic, having a base in one place but working in other places for part of the week, for individual days, or even for specific sessions each week.

How therapists work

How therapists work and offer their therapy will differ too. For example, some therapists working in mainstream schools may decide to visit several schools for an intensive period, such as every day for a term. This would then be followed by a period of 'no therapy' to those schools while the therapist moves to offer intensive therapy to other schools within the area. This pattern would then be repeated over a period of months throughout the year.

In other places, such as in nurseries or when working with people with learning disabilities, therapists may prefer to train the staff to work with the clients. The therapist will then work in each setting possibly once a week, liaising with the staff and dealing with any queries. They may work individually with a few clients with more complex problems.

Within a clinical setting a therapist may visit a patient on the ward on a daily basis. Once the patient leaves hospital they may attend for therapy in the hospital's outpatients' department. At this stage the therapist may offer some clients a period of intensive therapy followed by a break, followed by a further period of intensive therapy. Others may choose to see clients on a weekly basis.

Therapists may work alone or in teams with other speech

and language therapists depending on the resources available. They may also work in multi-disciplinary teams where they would be the only speech and language therapist.

Specialists

Sometimes within a service there may be therapists who are specialists, for example, in working with people who stammer. Such therapists may be based permanently on one site with all the clients with stammering problems being referred to them. Alternatively, in the children's service, the specialist therapist may travel across the area visiting all the children with those specific problems at different clinics, in schools or even in their own homes.

Sometimes there are specialist services in centres of excellence located in a specific place and people may be referred there from other parts of the country. Such services are offered by specialist teams such as in neurological units, cochlear implant centres, cleft palate centres, or in centres that specialise in working with people who stammer.

Different settings in health and education in the UK

Depending on how the service is organised some therapists may work in several different settings during the course of the week. For example, a newly qualified therapist in a first job may work with adults for the first part of the week and with children for the remainder of the week. Of course, this will be on different sites.

A peripatetic therapist working on many different sites, will run sessions in several different places during the course of a week. Such therapists joke that they develop strong shoulders from carrying their equipment from one place to the other and they learn how to snatch lunch on the run!

As peripatetic therapists are always on the move they

will usually have a base where they can be contacted and where they hold most of their files and paperwork. Sometimes the service may provide the therapist with a mobile phone. Normally, at this base a therapist would expect to have a filing cabinet, possibly a computer and a cupboard designated to speech and language therapy in which they can keep any equipment and assessments, any instrumentation, and any books and activities which can be used in therapy; and there may be several therapists using the same base. However, as it is unlikely that all assessments and equipment needed for therapy will be available at each base it may be necessary to transport materials from one place to another. Therapists within a specific geographical area may often share equipment.

Most therapists do not have a dedicated speech and language therapy room in every place they work and often have to share their room with other professionals, particularly if they do not occupy that room every day.

Clinics

If the setting is a health centre or community clinic, often just referred to as a 'clinic', there will usually be other health professionals within the same setting. They may well share a receptionist and possibly some secretarial support. Some therapists work full-time in such settings. Others may work there for only part of the week, moving to other settings on specific days.

Schools

Some therapists work in school settings. This could be within mainstream or special schools, units or nurseries. They may be employed to work only in one school and sometimes may even be employed by that school. More commonly, however, they will visit several schools, the number depending on the resources within the area.

In this setting therapists naturally work closely with the teaching staff and will spend much of their time working with the children within the classroom. They will find that much of their collaborative work and informal meetings will take place with teachers and LSAs over a quickly snatched cup of coffee in the staff room. Therapists in such settings are unlikely to have their own rooms. However, if they work full-time within the school they may have their own room where they can withdraw any children individually.

Child Development Centres

Children who have definite medical or neurological problems would attend a Child Development Centre that may be part of a hospital. The speech and language therapist would normally be part of the team of health professionals dealing with such children. Therapists may often share accommodation with other members of the team. If the centre is attached to a hospital the therapist may also be involved in ward rounds with other members of the multi-disciplinary team.

Hospital outpatients

There are paediatric speech and language therapy clinics attached to some hospital outpatient departments and adult speech and language therapy clinics attached to others. There may be some hospitals that have both, although the two are usually run separately by different therapy teams.

Adults may also be seen in rehabilitation departments of large hospitals or in special rehabilitation units or centres.

Hospitals

Many adults, particularly those with head injuries or having suffered a stroke, are seen in the acute wards of hospitals during the early stages of their recovery. Later, once they have been discharged, they may be seen as an outpatient. Therapists in hospitals usually work as part of a multi-disciplinary team and often share accommodation with other team members.

Other settings

People with communication problems who are elderly, or have learning disabilities or sometimes mental health problems may be seen within day centres or possibly within a care home or some other form of residential setting. Some specialist speech and language therapists work with people with psychiatric problems within secure units or secure hospitals.

Home visiting – domiciliary work

A few therapists conduct the majority of their work through domiciliary visits actually working with the clients within their home. There are advantages to such an approach as it is often helpful to see clients in their natural contexts. However, from a resources point of view, it is not cost effective to spend too much time travelling to individual places.

More commonly therapists will make an occasional home visit. This may occur when working with adults, although most often home visits will be made by therapists working with young children particularly those with multiple difficulties.

Working in the voluntary sector

Qualified therapists may choose to work for one of the voluntary organisations associated with people with communication difficulties.

Working in the independent or private sector

There are also opportunities for therapists to work with clients privately. Sometimes this would be in addition to a day job, or some therapists work independently either by setting up a private practice or by working in a private hospital or a private school.

Working as a locum, 'agency working'

There are now many agencies that employ speech and language therapists. Locum work will often be available when, for example, someone has taken maternity leave or is given extended leave of absence.

Some Trusts employ agency staff when they are unable to fill a post with permanent staff. Short term and longer term posts may become available through an agency and therapists will be assigned the work in much the same way as they would if they were an agency nurse or a temp typist.

When undertaking agency work, therapists need to prove that they meet the qualification and registration requirements in the same way as they would for any speech and language therapy job; only the employment conditions will be different.

Working abroad

Therapists might work abroad in two different ways. One is on a voluntary basis for example through Voluntary Service Overseas (VSO); the other is being employed as a speech and language therapist in another country. If you are fluent in another relevant language you may be able to work in another country within the EU. See also *Can I work abroad with the qualification?* Chapter 1 and *What if you want to work overseas?* Chapter 33.

Chapter 7 What a speech and language therapist does

When we say we are speech and language therapists the most common response is, 'Oh good, then you can teach me to talk properly'. But this is NOT TRUE. That is definitely not part of the speech and language therapist's role. However, there do seem to be many popular misconceptions about speech and language therapy, so we shall begin this next part by dispelling some of the myths.

Before you read the following you might like to do a check for yourself and see if you can write down six things that you think a speech and language therapist does.

*Figure 5 **What you think a speech and language therapist does***

1
2
3
4
5
6

Let us start by considering what a speech and language therapist does *not* do.

Figure 6 What speech and language therapists are not

- They are not elocution teachers.
- They do not help people to 'talk properly', 'talk posh' or 'talk better'.
- In the UK therapists are not concerned with accent reduction for people who speak with a regional accent or for those who speak English as an additional language.
- They are not nurses.
- They are not subsidiary to doctors.
- They are not teachers.
- They are not counsellors or psychotherapists.
- They are not voice coaches.
- Therapists themselves do not necessarily need to speak using 'received pronunciation' (what is often referred to as 'BBC English').

The next most common response to saying we are speech and language therapists is, 'It must be very rewarding'. That is true and you may not find it so surprising if you consider the next list which looks at what speech and language therapists really are.

Figure 7 What speech and language therapists are

- They are the therapists helping to improve speech when there is a specific physical, pathological, or possibly psychological reason for the poor speech.
- They are the therapists who provide people with a means of communication, for example, offering alternative approaches to people who are unable to speak.
- They are the therapists who help people to develop language when there is a specific physical, pathological, or possibly psychological reason for their limited language.
- They are the therapists who help people who have specific physical, pathological, or possibly psychological difficulties with their voice.
- They are the therapists who work with people who for physical or possibly psychological reasons are unable to speak fluently.
- They are the therapists who work with people from a multi-cultural background when there is an underlying problem affecting all languages spoken.
- They are health professionals and work independently, closely alongside nurses and doctors.
- They are also involved closely in education.
- They carry out their own assessment.
- They make their own diagnostic decisions regarding communication and swallowing problems.
- They make their own management decisions about how to deal with communication or swallowing problems.
- They plan and implement therapy relating to communication and swallowing problems.
- They may train others to help implement the therapy.
- They are facilitators supporting and encouraging.
- They may sometimes take on a counselling role.
- They may be concerned with 'vocal hygiene' helping people to preserve and protect their voices.
- As speech and language therapists they do have to be good communicators and articulate clearly and a regional accent may often be an advantage.

A speech and language therapy job description

If we were to draw up a general job description for a speech and language therapist without including the details of a specific job it might look something like this.

Figure 8 A speech and language therapy job description

Job summary for full-time post   **_10 sessions per week_**

The post-holder must be an HPC registered speech and language therapist. S/he must be able to work independently, managing their own caseload in accordance with the Trust's guidelines while maintaining the standards required by the Trust and by the professional body. S/he will take full responsibility for the clients, while being accountable to the speech and language therapy manager.

Salary Scales see RCSLT website for latest salary details.

Main duties and responsibilities
The post holder must be able to:
- Organise and manage the caseload.
- Assess clients as appropriate by observing and evaluating their communicative strengths and weakness and gathering any other appropriate information.
- Make a differential diagnosis of the problem.
- Decide whether therapy is needed.
- Implement the therapy directly or train others to implement the therapy as appropriate.
- Offer help and advice to relatives and friends of the client as needed.
- Liaise with colleagues as required.

- Keep records, write reports, letters, and complete all administrative tasks required.
- Complete statistical returns for the PCT or local authority.
- Attend meetings, annual reviews.
- Work with students.
- Continue professional learning through reading, attending courses or conferences.
- Monitor and evaluate the service in accordance with local guidelines.
- Actively follow local policies including Equal Opportunities and Race Equality policies.
- Maintain an awareness and observation of Fire and Health & Safety Regulations.

What a speech and language therapist needs to know

If we think back to the speech and language chain, or communication chain, we can begin to understand some of the knowledge and skills that a speech and language therapist needs in order to carry out the job described above. It is this body of knowledge – understanding how human communication works and how and why it breaks down – that student speech and language therapists must acquire through their studies. Such knowledge will help them to develop the appropriate skills for dealing with people with a whole range of speech, language and communication problems.

Figure 9 *The skills and knowledge required to understand speech and language*

The skills required for human communication	The knowledge required to understand the development of these skills
❑ Mental ability to initiate the first thought or think of an appropriate response. ❑ Mental ability to process and interpret verbal and non-verbal messages. ❑ The ability to concentrate and attend to the words of the speaker.	❑ Understanding of people's cognitive and emotional development and their behaviour through the study of different aspects of psychology.
❑ The development of a common language with the speaker so that the message can expressed, received and understood. ❑ The linguistic ability to find the words for the initial message and response.	❑ Knowledge of linguistics, psycholinguistics and speech and language acquisition. ❑ Ability to transcribe and analyse speech and language.
❑ The physical ability to speak the words out loud.	❑ Knowledge of the anatomy and physiology of the body, the brain and neurology particularly relating to speech production.
❑ Ability of the speaker to monitor that what was said is what was intended.	❑ Knowledge of how we monitor our own speech and language.
❑ Acuity of hearing to receive the spoken message accurately.	❑ Knowledge of acoustics and audiology to understand the hearing mechanism.

You will, therefore, cover the following subjects on any course leading to a qualification as a speech and language therapist.

Figure 10 Brief summary of subject areas studied

• linguistics • psycholinguistics • language acquisition	• psychology • education/sociology • audiology • physical development	• speech/language pathology • medical aspects • neurological aspects

What a qualified therapist actually does

People wanting to become speech and language therapists usually say they need 'to feel they are making a difference'. Mature students at interview, especially those who are considering a change of career, usually add that they need 'to know that what they are doing is important'.

If we consider what a speech and language therapist actually does then you will be able to make up your own mind about its importance and how much difference you might be making to someone else's life.

✓ Speech and language therapists are concerned with helping people communicate, either helping them develop their communication or helping them regain their communication when it has broken down.

✓ They work alongside other professionals, often as part of a team, making independent diagnoses of the problems and deciding how to manage them. These problems may involve communication and/or eating, drinking and swallowing problems in children and adults.

✓ Normally, during the course of a day, they will see several individual clients or small groups and possibly attend some meetings or reviews. They will spend time, often at the end of the day, recording notes, writing reports, making telephone calls and keeping statistical records.

✓ If they do not work directly with clients, then their day might be taken up training others, running workshops, monitoring the work of the staff or relatives they have trained, evaluating the progress of the clients and attending meetings or reviews.

✓ Some therapists will work with speech and language therapy assistants and most will supervise students on placement, which can be of enormous mutual benefit. In such instances the therapist will assign, discuss and monitor appropriate work for the assistants/students to do.

Whether dealing with a communication or a swallowing problem, the way in which a speech and language therapist proceeds normally follows a general pattern, irrespective of the nature of the specific job. This generic pattern is outlined below.

Figure 11 Flow chart of the speech and language therapy process

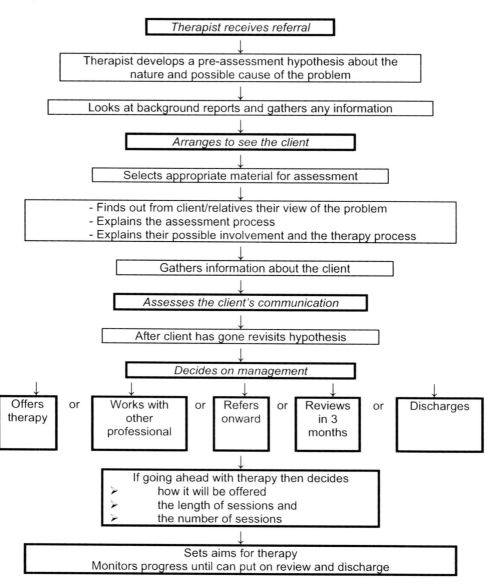

Therapist receives referral

Therapist develops a pre-assessment hypothesis about the nature and possible cause of the problem

Looks at background reports and gathers any information

Arranges to see the client

Selects appropriate material for assessment

- Finds out from client/relatives their view of the problem
- Explains the assessment process
- Explains their possible involvement and the therapy process

Gathers information about the client

Assesses the client's communication

After client has gone revisits hypothesis

Decides on management

| Offers therapy | or | Works with other professional | or | Refers onward | or | Reviews in 3 months | or | Discharges |

If going ahead with therapy then decides
- how it will be offered
- the length of sessions and
- the number of sessions

Sets aims for therapy
Monitors progress until can put on review and discharge

Forming a hypothesis

The therapist puts together the initial information and tries to work out what the problem might be, and to decide about the nature of the assessment that will help give the maximum information about the client and the problem.

Assessment and gathering information

Assessment takes the form of observing directly as well as finding out from others about the client's problem. The therapist will try to find out how the problem is manifest and how the client communicates in different situations.

More formal background information or a 'case history' is usually gathered by the therapist. This will include relevant medical details, social history, and the history of the problem. This information can be gleaned from several different sources. It may come from parents, if working with children; or from the relatives and friends of adults; from the clients themselves; from letters and reports from other professionals; from speaking directly to other professionals such as teachers, doctors or physiotherapists, and from the initial referral sheet.

The therapist is then able to use the information together with his/her own knowledge about the problem to draw some conclusions about whether there is anything wrong; if something is wrong to decide what that might be, and to see whether the initial hypothesis was correct. The therapist can then make decisions about how best to offer help.

If it is appropriate to offer therapy, then aims are set for what the client hopes to achieve. These can then be monitored and checked. If the aims are not being achieved it may be necessary to reassess the situation. When all the goals have been met, therapy should no longer be needed.

Therapy

Therapy will take different forms and will obviously differ according to whether you are working with adults or with children. Mostly, with any client group, therapy involves some form of talking and listening.

When working with people with physical disabilities in order to communicate it may involve the use of a communication aid and with deaf people it may involve the use of BSL instead of speech.

Sometimes, specifically designed computer programmes can be helpful as a therapy tool particularly as they will give immediate visual or auditory feedback and the clients are often able to work independently with them.

If you are observing a therapist working with a client it may all look deceivingly easy but, as discussed in the *frequently asked questions,* in Chapter 1, this is the therapists' skill. Therapists in fact are carefully juggling several activities at once. They observe the client; while recalling the relevant theoretical knowledge; while adding the newly gained information; while concentrating on the task in hand, at the same time as monitoring the client's behaviour. They need then to come to some decisions quickly. If the tasks are proving too easy for the client, or too difficult, therapists need 'to think on their feet' so that they can adjust the level of difficulty of the task immediately and without the client realising.

Activities

Therapists use a variety of activities depending on the age of the client and the nature of the problem and the client's interests. These may vary from carefully structured play, to specifically devised 'games', use of pictures, or reading and writing. The purpose of any activity must always be to enable the therapy goal to be reached while helping to maintain the client's interest and motivation. For example, games and exercises may be specifically devised to help children or adults achieve target words, or to understand phrases with which they are having difficulty.

Discharging clients

At the end of a period of therapy it may be that the client can be discharged, either because the problem is 'cured' or because they have progressed as far as possible. It may be that the client's progress has reached a 'plateau' so that they have progressed as far as they can for the moment. Then, they will be put 'on review' and seen again several months later.

Therapy sessions

Although the aims and activities will differ according to the client and the nature of the problem, therapy sessions will follow a pattern and this will be true whether working with individual clients or with a small group. While working within any therapy session the therapist will:

- prepare and finalise the aims and objectives for the session;
- devise activities to help meet the aims and objectives;
- prepare the activities for the session;
- use the activities for assessment or therapy;
- monitor if the level of activity is too difficult or too easy;
- evaluate the session to see if the aims and objectives have been achieved;
- evaluate the client's general progress;
- if appropriate, ask the client to continue with some work outside of the session possibly involving parents, relatives, assistants;
- arrange another session;

- write up the notes from the session;
- consider the aims and objectives of the next session.

Sample session

Connor is three years old and has delayed speech and language and immature play. Spontaneously he uses single words occasionally such as 'Mummy', 'Daddy', and 'you' to get attention although he has been heard to use several other words as well. He mostly expresses himself by using gestures and vocalisations. He can understand and follow simple commands such as, 'find the car', 'put the garage away on the shelf' in a specific play context. He attends with his mother for a forty-five minute therapy session each week.

Aims

The main aims for Connor's therapy are to encourage him to use more spoken language and to widen the scope of his play.

Objective

The specific objective for this session is for Connor to use at least three words from his word pool of 'car, man, garage, go, drive', either singly or combined at least once.

Activities

☐ To play with miniature cars, people, garage on a play mat marked out with a road, trees and children's playground.
☐ To have additional toys available such as a car wash, a garage lift and petrol pumps, as well as different types of vehicles.
☐ To look at books with pictures of assorted cars and people.
☐ To cut out pictures of cars from a catalogue or magazine

and stick them in a book for Connor to take home.

His mother is invited into the room to join in with the session. The therapist, Lucy discusses progress with his mother and begins to play with Connor. This provides a model for how to encourage him to use the appropriate words without asking him to 'say this', or 'what's that', and provides a model for how to encourage him to widen the scope of his activities.

- Lucy starts with a play session, on the floor, with Connor and his mother.
- She initiates the play.
- After ten to fifteen minutes, Lucy sits back and observes Connor and his mother while making notes of all the words he utters, transcribing them in phonetic script so that she can later analyse if there are any problems with his speech as well as his language.
- When they all sit together at the table looking at books, Lucy is monitoring Connor's reactions to the books she has chosen and quickly realises the pictures are too complex for him to distinguish the individual items.
- Lucy chooses some simpler pictures from the cupboard.
- She praises any new words Connor utters and repeats them, dropping them into her own conversation without drawing particular attention to them.

- At the end of the session Lucy notes that Connor did begin to use all the additional toys she provided and the fact that he used more words than previously, so fulfilling the aims of the session.
- Lucy has recorded that Connor used the word 'man' three times, 'car' six times, 'car go' once, and 'go garage' once, so achieving the session objective. This is marked progress, as it is the first time he has put two

words together in this way.

- During a discussion of the session afterwards, his mother reports that Connor has never done that at home.
- Connor takes away his book with stickers for his effort and achievement, and the promise to show it to his siblings and tell them about the session.
- An appointment is arranged for the same time next week.
- After they have gone, Lucy briefly records the main features of the session.
- Lucy notes that she will continue with the same aims next week, but she will make the objective more difficult so that she can work towards increasing the vocabulary Connor is beginning to use. She will also introduce different toys to widen the scope of his play still further. She also makes a note to discuss with his mother the possibility of visiting Connor at his nursery.

Do all clients make progress?

Communication problems cannot be helped by taking a tablet and often a complete 'cure' or resolution of the problem is not always possible. For example, people who stammer may improve greatly, but there can be no 100% guarantee that the stammer will not return, requiring further work at some stage.

Of course in many instances, particularly with young children, it may be possible after a period of therapy for their communication to become 'normal', but at other times therapy is about helping the person make the best use of what they have. For example, with people who have had a head injury or a stroke, their medical condition may mean that there are limitations to the recovery that can be made, but that does not mean that they won't make progress. In other cases, such as with people with severe or profound and multiple learning disabilities, depending on the degree of disability, progress may be limited.

People who have severe physical disabilities may not be able to speak and may rely instead on some form of augmentative and alternative communication system (AAC) such as a picture board or a symbol board to point to, or some kind of electronic communication aid. In such instances, it is important for the therapist to adjust the expectations so that, through realistically set goals, small steps of change will help the clients to achieve as much as possible.

Accepting slow progress

You will, therefore, need to be prepared within the scope of the work, for progress to be slow and to accept that the end-product is not necessarily 'perfection'. While it is rewarding to be able to help someone make changes in their communication, you need to be able to deal with the frustration of sometimes seeing them make only small amounts of progress. Sometimes therapy is about maintenance, such as with a progressive disease, where you will need to make sure clients continue to be able to use their communication skills to their maximum. But, if you can help someone achieve their potential – often achieving things they never thought possible – if you can prevent their difficulty from becoming a handicap, then you will find the work very rewarding indeed.

Chapter 8 The skills and qualities needed as a speech and language therapy student

Having discussed some of the details of the job in the previous chapter, it is now time to think about you, and to consider whether you have the appropriate skills and qualities to become a therapist. Let's begin with another question:

'What attracted you to think about speech and language therapy as a possible career?'

Figure 12 The attractions of speech and language therapy as a career

You might have included:

> ➤ I love language.
> ➤ I'm a good communicator and would like to help others who can't communicate as I realise how frustrating it is.
> ➤ I want to work with people.
> ➤ My grandmother had a stroke and I felt helpless.
> ➤ My sister has Down Syndrome and I want to be able to help other children like her.
> ➤ My friend had a motorcycle accident and I want to be able to help.
> ➤ I have a degree in linguistics and want to use my analytical skills.
> ➤ I am interested in how language and communication works.

These are all perfectly valid reasons for beginning to think about speech and language therapy as a career, and a good place to start. But, in order to take your initial attraction to its final conclusion and to complete the education and training successfully, you will need more than that. You will need application, hard work and dedication to keep you motivated for the duration of your studies. You will also need the ability to develop some of the specific qualities and skills required to work successfully as a speech and language therapist.

So, let's consider the answer to another commonly asked question:

'Do I need to be a special kind of person to become a speech and language therapist?'

We can then think about what you need in order to help you stay the course and become a therapist.

Once qualified you will need a wide range of knowledge and skills to help you to work effectively as a therapist, and you will also need to have developed the qualities that will help you adopt the appropriate professional attitude to your work. You will probably find you have already begun to develop some of the skills and qualities that will make you into a good therapist, such as the ability be a good listener. However, even such existing skills will need to be developed further if they are to be used appropriately within the professional role.

For example, you will find that within the professional context there is more to listening than merely 'being a good listener' and you will need to develop more active listening skills. Similarly, you may be a good communicator in social settings, but you will need to refine and hone your interpersonal skills so that, for example, you are able to present complex technical material in an understandable form, such as when talking to parents.

During a speech and language therapy course you will develop such skills so that you will be able to work professionally in any of the roles described earlier. You will also learn specific skills, such as the ability to transcribe speech quickly and accurately in phonetic script, – a skill which is new to most students and one you may need to acquire from scratch.

A person specification – skills, qualities and experience

A person specification for any job describes the skills, qualities and experience required by the post holder and states whether these are 'essential' to the job or merely 'desirable'.

As a new student you will not be expected to have all of these essential or desirable qualities or skills but, as there is much competition for entry onto speech and language therapy courses, especially the post-graduate courses, the more you have and the more you are able to demonstrate that you have the ability to develop, the better chance you will have of being selected.

So, let's consider the qualities, skills and experience that you may be bringing to the course and that you will be developing during the course in order to practise successfully as a speech and language therapist. This is presented in Figure 13 and discussed in detail on the following pages.

Figure 13 Person specification – for a speech and language therapy student

Requirements	Essential	Desirable
Skills and abilities	❖ Proven ability to be able to study at relevant degree level ❖ Good oral communication skills ❖ Good interpersonal skills ❖ Be an 'active' listener ❖ Ability to cope with others' distress ❖ Ability to cope with your own distress ❖ Ability to cope with minimal change in the client ❖ Reflection and evaluation skills ❖ Analytical skills ❖ Ability to synthesise ❖ Independence ❖ Ability to take responsibility ❖ Ability to learn new IT skills	❖ Good written-communication skills ❖ Organisational skills ❖ Problem-solving skills ❖ Assertiveness ❖ Team skills ❖ Ability to give appropriate feedback

Personal qualities	❖ Enthusiasm ❖ Commitment to hard work ❖ Self motivation ❖ Intellectual curiosity ❖ Be interested in people ❖ Creativity ❖ Warmth ❖ Empathy ❖ Initiative ❖ Adaptability and flexibility ❖ Self awareness ❖ Non-judgemental approach	❖ Caring ❖ Be able to receive feedback ❖ Ability to cope with uncertainty ❖ Patience
Experience	❖ Talked to a therapist ❖ Worked with or talked to people with communication difficulties	❖ Seen a therapist at work – live or on video

Essential skills

Ability to study

You will need to show your ability to study at degree level. If you are applying straight from school, you will be able to prove your ability to study by producing the appropriately successful 'A' level results, or Scottish or Irish 'Highers', or the International Baccalaureate. Mature students may successfully conclude an Access Course if applying for an undergraduate degree.

If you are interested in post-graduate study you can prove your ability by obtaining a good classification in your first degree, preferably a 1st or a 2:1.

If you are a mature student and have not studied for several years, it will probably be helpful if you are able to demonstrate a recent ability to study by obtaining a relevant AS level prior to application. A subject such as human biology or psychology would be useful.

Oral communication skills

All your skills will no doubt improve and develop during the course but you will need to be a good communicator before you begin. You will be able to demonstrate this in several ways if you are interviewed, for example by the confidence you demonstrate in your manner of greeting, in the way you sit and stand, in your ability to make eye contact and in your voice.

During the course you will also learn more about presentation skills making audio- and video-recordings. You will have opportunities to present complex information in a simple and understandable way to an audience using visual aids and will possibly have to answer questions about your chosen subject. These will prove important skills on the job, as many therapists have to make presentations to professional colleagues and parents.

Interpersonal skills

Good interpersonal skills will enable you to forge good working relationships, which will be essential for working within your own peer student group as well as when working collaboratively and in teams with other professionals while on placement. You will also be working with people whose speech and communication patterns differ from the norm, so you will constantly need to be able to modify your communication according to the needs of individual clients.

Interpersonal skills include, for example, the ability to listen to others without making judgemental assumptions and responding to them in an appropriate way, showing that you are aware of their needs.

Be an active listener

Most students feel they begin the course being 'good listeners' and this is an essential underlying skill if you are to acquire successfully the ability for 'active listening'. Active listening, however, is a more complex process than 'good listening' as you need to be open to hearing and understanding someone's message without prejudice or assumptions and, where necessary, offer a carefully considered response.

This does not mean saying, 'I know what you mean, the same thing happened to me...', or being able to offer advice. To be an active listener in a therapy situation you need to analyse, process and synthesise the information in a more formal and organised way and, having considered the information, to respond appropriately by commenting, or by reflecting the words back to the speaker in a specific way, or sometimes by just sitting with the speaker in silence.

Ability to cope with others' distress

If you cannot cope with other people's distress, then 'look away now'. Very often clients, or their families are distressed by their situation, the problem itself, their frustration, and the possible future. In addition, certain conditions, such as a stroke, often makes someone much more likely to burst into tears even without a specific cause. You need to be able to cope with this, or to be prepared to learn how to cope with such situations if they occur within the therapy setting. You will be helped with this during the course, particularly while on placement.

Ability to cope with your own distress and feelings

You must also be aware of the emotional demands of being a therapist and how this might affect you. This is a challenge on any course involving a clinical therapy training and can be particular difficult for those on the two year Master's courses where students learn at an accelerated rate, with little time for their own social and emotional lives.

For example, you may be dealing with clients who remind you of one of your own friends or relatives who has sustained a serious injury or suffered an illness. This can obviously prove distressing.

Equally students may become distressed by the sadness of someone else's plight, and find it difficult listening to their story and seeing their frustration. There may be an additional element of your own frustration if progress is slow when working with that particular client. In such situations you must be prepared to learn to keep a professional distance, to empathise and show an understanding of the problem without bursting into sympathetic, but inappropriate, tears yourself.

Part of being a professional is keeping such feelings under control and learning how to maintain professional boundaries with the clients and their families.

Ability to cope with minimal change in clients

As discussed earlier, therapy is not always about effecting a 'cure' and sometimes the accepted level of change or progress made is very small. This may often prove frustrating for the therapist, but it is something you will have to be prepared to accept.

Reflection and evaluation skills

These skills normally begin to develop while at school. You will need to be able to stand back, to review an activity or task and to evaluate critically your own performance. You will need to be able to accept feedback from others, and to give appropriate feedback to them. You will then need to think about any changes that need to be made to enhance and improve your performance.

Analytical skills

You will probably have some level of analytical skills that you have used in your previous studies. However, you will need to use them in different ways on a speech and language therapy course after you have acquired the requisite knowledge. For example, having learned about different aspects of phonetics and linguistics you will need to be able to analyse your clients' speech and language phonetically and linguistically. You will learn to analyse the results of any assessments you administer. You will also learn how to analyse data statistically.

Ability to synthesise

You will need to be able to gather information from a variety of sources such as, for example, when conducting a library search among journals, books, websites, and any other reference sources. Having located this information, you will then need to be able to draw it together in a meaningful way, in much the same way as you will need to do when putting together your personal statement on your application form.

When working in a clinic, you will need to make decisions based on information gathered about a client so that you will need to synthesise all the information in order to plan appropriate action.

Independence

You may already have demonstrated your ability to work independently prior to course entry. In order to work successfully on placement during the course, you will need to show that you can work with the minimum of supervision even in unfamiliar surroundings and situations. Although you may work with other students, a supervising clinician will expect you to show that, with support, you are able to work on your own.

Ability to take responsibility

This is another area where you may already have demonstrated your abilities. As a student you would be expected to take responsibility for your own learning, taking the initiative, undertaking much independent study and ensuring that you have whatever you need in order to help you learn. When on placement you will be expected to take responsibility for a small number of clients, with support and supervision from your supervising clinician.

Ability to learn new technological skills

Students today are mostly expected to word process their written work and to be able to access, process and deliver information through electronic means, although this will vary according to the university. It will be essential, however, that you are not techno-phobic and are able to learn word-processing and other IT skills.

Desirable skills

Written-communication skills

It will help your studies if you already have good written skills as you will need to adopt different writing styles depending on whether you are writing an essay, a report or you are recording succinct case notes. Of course, this does not necessarily preclude you if you have any specific reading and spelling problems. You would need to achieve the basic university entry requirements and how you would manage any specific difficulties could be discussed with the Course Tutor.

Organisational skills

You will need to be able to organise yourself, your time and your work if you are to cope with all the different college-based subjects at the same time as you are planning, preparing and working on placement. There will be coursework, tests and examinations, in the different study areas, many of which will have long-term deadlines, and you will need to develop time management skills in order to be able to cope with these satisfactorily and prepare your work on time. On placement you will need to show good organisational skills so that you will be able to work like a 'professional therapist'.

Problem-solving skills

Many people take a problem-solving approach to aspects of their lives, negotiating their way around obstacles and developing effective strategies for overcoming them. When on placement, you will need to take a problem-solving approach to your work if you are to be able to design effective therapy to help clients achieve their objectives.

Assertiveness

Many people confuse assertiveness with aggressiveness, but as a speech and language therapy student you will need to learn to be assertive, putting forward your point of view firmly but without being aggressive, if you are to be heard in your year group. Equally you must not be afraid to speak out and ask appropriate questions so that you get the most out of tutorials, seminars and lectures. You will also need to be able to speak up for yourself in a non-aggressive way when working on placement, particularly when learning to work as a fellow professional alongside your supervising clinician and when beginning to work collaboratively with other professionals.

You will need to develop a strong voice, without sounding strident, and a pleasant but firm manner that does not appear confrontational. This will help you when you have to negotiate with clients, their families, with your supervising clinician and with other colleagues.

Team skills

Some people will already show early signs of group leadership before beginning the course, or will show that they are able to develop these skills as the course progresses. This will not only prove helpful when working with colleagues and peers, but when managing, guiding or facilitating groups of clients.

Being able to work as part of a group or team is an essential aspect of speech and language therapy, both as a student and as a therapist. You will need to show that you are able to co-operate with others and contribute to group activities. Being a 'team player' will help you to get along with your fellow students as many tutorials and seminars rely on group-work and group co-operation. You may find yourself working closely with other students while on placement and this will be good training for working as part of a team as a therapist when the first lesson you will learn is how to get along with people you might not necessarily chose as your friends.

Ability to give appropriate feedback

Giving feedback which is appropriate that is, feedback that is specific enough for the person to be able to act on and change their behaviour, that is given in such a way as not to be offensive, is a skill which some people may already have. If not, it is something that will develop during the course.

Essential qualities

Most of the qualities required to become a speech and language therapy student, and ultimately a therapist, speak for themselves. Qualities such as enthusiasm, commitment to hard work and self-motivation need no further explanation.

Intellectual curiosity

Intellectual curiosity will help to motivate you and keep you interested in all aspects of the work. You will always want to know that little bit more than the lecturers tell you and will be motivated to further self-study.

This will help you not only as a student, but will encourage you to continue your learning, understanding the need for undertaking continuing professional development.

Interest in people

This too may sound an obvious quality but you need to be interested in people in different ways. You need to enjoy being involved with people from all walks of life and to enjoy working with them. But, you also need to be interested in helping to disentangle their often complex and difficult problems, recognising and accommodating the fact that they have differing needs, feelings and behaviour.

Creativity

This applies not only to the ability to invent creative activities, interesting games and innovative ways of delivering therapy, but also to the ability to think laterally and inventively about issues, particularly when working with clients, and to develop original approaches to defining and solving clinical problems.

Warmth and empathy

'Warmth, empathy and genuineness' are said to be among the essential ingredients for those undertaking any form of counselling and therapy work and this is no less true of speech and language therapists. Therapists must be able to hold their clients in what is called 'unconditional positive regard' that is, to stand outside of their own natural prejudices and biases and to concentrate on a 'client is right' approach, so that they can help their clients' to work with their problems to the best of their ability.

This is not about you feeling sympathy for your clients, but you trying to understand how they might be feeling, and trying to see things from their point of view.

Initiative

It is essential for you to be able to take initiative as a student, particularly if you taking responsibility for your own learning. This is never more true than when working on placement when your supervisor will expect you to do more than sit waiting to be told what to do, but will expect you to initiate activities and follow your interests without prompting.

You can demonstrate this ability before you complete your application form by taking the initiative to find appropriate books to read about your intended career, to meet and work with people with communication problems, or to visit clinics and talk to therapists.

Adaptability and flexibility

All therapy is about change, enabling and facilitating change in others and being able to make changes in your own behaviour so that you can adjust to changing circumstances and new challenges. As a student you will need to be able to adjust constantly to your new life and to the challenges of the work. As a student-therapist working on placement, you will need to be flexible in your approach to therapy so that you are constantly monitoring and adjusting the work to an appropriate level for the client.

Self-awareness

It is important to be able to evaluate your own strengths, areas which could be improved and to mark your own progress. However, even more critically on such a therapy course, it is important to be aware of your own value systems, to be able to analyse your own prejudices and biases and be aware of how you view others, for example, people of a different culture, people who speak other languages, or people with disabilities. It is easy to say, 'I'm not prejudiced; I'm very tolerant.' We all have our prejudices and there is always something we cannot tolerate. What is more important is that we recognise what these are so that we can manage and control our feelings appropriately.

Non-judgemental approach

You need to ensure that any judgements and interpretations made are based solely on sound observation of behaviour and knowledge. For example, if a little boy runs into the clinic room and hides under the table, you cannot judge him and label him as 'naughty' without knowing all the facts. You can only comment that he ran straight into the room and under the table. He may have acted in this way for any number of reasons.
- The room was too bright and the light hurt his eyes.
- He had been there before and been frightened by the experience so wanted to hide.
- He constantly plays hide and seek under the table at home.

- He had been playing hide and seek with his brother in the waiting room and was merely extending the game.
- He wanted to tease and exasperate his mother.
- He is extremely shy of strangers and the table was the only place he could hide from you.
- His mother had told him he could sit under the table if he wanted.

There may be any number of possible explanations for a simple action so it is important to be sure of your facts and to try and work out why someone behaved as they did before jumping to possibly false conclusions.

Desirable qualities

Caring

Of course, you will need to be a caring person or you would not be interested in helping others, but caring is only one of many qualities and it is not enough on its own.

Being able to receive feedback

You will receive much feedback during the course from a variety of sources and you will need to be able to accept such feedback without reacting defensively, appreciate that it is not personally getting at you, and learn how to use the feedback to change your behaviour in order to help you develop your skills.

Ability to cope with uncertainty

If you are someone who likes to have 'cut and dried' answers or likes to feel there is a right or a wrong way of doing something, then speech and language therapy is not the career for you. In speech and language therapy there is rarely only one way to tackle a problem, there is rarely an absolutely right or absolutely wrong approach. You need to be able to accept this level of uncertainty.

Patience

Contrary to what most people think, patience is a desirable rather than an essential quality for a speech and language therapist and you would be wrong to imagine that all therapists are the most patient people in the world. Of course you will need to show patience with your clients and not lose your temper or show impatience in any way, but that does not mean that in other circumstances you are necessarily the most patient person in your personal life.

Experience

It is essential before applying that you have a real idea of what it means to have a communication difficulty and what speech and language therapists do about such problems. It is, therefore, important that you meet people with communication difficulties, such as elderly people in nursing care, children in special schools, children or adults with learning disabilities, or deaf people. Ideally, you should work with them on a voluntary or paid basis. This is definitely desirable and in many universities it will be considered essential, particularly if you are applying for one of the post-graduate courses where you may be expected to show considerable experience.

Similarly, you must try to talk to a therapist, or to listen to a talk given by a therapist about the work that they do so that you have some direct knowledge of what their job entails.

Ideally, it would be helpful for you to watch a therapist at work, but it is accepted that this is not always possible. However, there are courses you might attend or books and possibly videos may be available from the library.

Summary

Of course, you will not necessarily have all of these skills and qualities before you apply for the course although you will need to develop a combination of such skills, qualities and experiences if you are to become a motivated student and ultimately a successful therapist. Hopefully you will start your course with good basic abilities and you will then build on these, developing your existing skills and learning new ones so that they can be synthesised with the knowledge you will learn on the course.

Chapter 9 The skills and qualities needed as a therapist

Once you have successfully completed a speech and language therapy course you will be in a position to apply for your first job as a speech and language therapist. By then you will have the essential knowledge and will have begun to develop your professional skills. You will also have laid the foundations for further skills' development, for example, if you want to study further, to become a specialist in a particular field, to become a manager possibly of a speech and language therapy department within the health service, or want to forge new directions such as in research.

Let us now consider the general requirements that would apply to most speech and language therapy jobs, allowing for the fact that specific jobs would also have their own person-specifications.

Figure 14 Essential requirements to work as a speech and language therapist

Requirements	Essential
Skills and abilities	❖ Understanding of the profession of speech and language therapy ❖ Commitment to continuing professional development ❖ Knowledge of speech and language pathology ❖ Acquisition of clinical skills re assessment and therapy ❖ Excellent oral communication skills ❖ Good written-communication skills ❖ Excellent interpersonal skills ❖ Analytical skills ❖ Ability to synthesise

	❖ Decision-making skills
	❖ Ability to organise yourself and your work
	❖ Ability to work independently with minimum supervision
	❖ Ability to take initiative
	❖ Ability to reflect
	❖ Ability to monitor and evaluate your work
	❖ Flexibility to adjust work levels according to clients' needs
	❖ Ability to work in teams
	❖ Ability to take responsibility
	❖ Proficiency in word processing
	❖ Ability to handle technology and learn new technological skills
	❖ Problem-solving skills
	❖ Ability to work collaboratively
	❖ Be a fully 'active' listener with the added ability of being able to respond
	❖ Assertiveness
	❖ Ability to cope with others' distress
	❖ Ability to cope with your own distress
	❖ Ability to cope with minimal change
	❖ Ability to give feedback
Personal qualities	❖ Enthusiasm
	❖ Commitment to hard work
	❖ Self motivation
	❖ Intellectual curiosity to want to continue learning
	❖ Be interested in people
	❖ Caring
	❖ Creativity
	❖ Warmth
	❖ Empathy
	❖ Initiative
	❖ Adaptability and flexibility
	❖ Non-judgemental approach
	❖ Ability to cope with uncertainty

	❖ Ability to receive feedback ❖ Patience
Experience	❖ Successfully completed all the clinical requirements of professional training ❖ Portfolio of work in a variety of clinical placements

You will see that the skills that were considered desirable before entry to the course are now essential for your progression to the workplace. But you don't have to worry that you don't have them all now, you will learn these as part of your course at university; just as you will learn all the speech and language pathology you need in order to start working as a therapist. By the time you start work you will also have had much experience working with a variety of people with a range of speech and language problems while on placement as part of your course.

Generalist not specialist

It is worth pointing out that you will not see people with every type of communication problem during your training; that is not possible in the time. Nor will you be qualified to work as a specialist in a specific area. The remit of any of the university courses is to ensure you have a good general speech and language therapy education including a breadth of diverse working experiences. This will then provide you with the foundation on which to begin your 'lifelong learning' in the workplace and to give you a solid basis from which to develop further skills should you wish to specialise.

Many people work with different client groups before deciding on an area of specialisation. They often think as students they want to work with one client group but find as they begin working that they change their minds. They may work on different areas in their continuing professional development (CPD) before focussing on an area in which to develop more specific expertise.

Essential skills

At first glance it may seem that the skills required by the qualified therapist are exactly the same as those required by the student therapist. This is true to some extent, although during the course you will acquire many new professional skills and will develop many of your existing skills and qualities to a different level; for you will find that many of the skills and qualities that you already had will be used in different ways within the professional context.

Interpersonal and communication skills

You will need to use these newly honed skills in order to establish yourself within your new workplace, to help you work collaboratively with individuals or as part of a team. You may also need your more highly developed presentation skills if training others is a part of your job, or if you present reports, take part in an annual review or ward round, or give a paper or poster at a conference.

Giving feedback

Not only will you be expected to give feedback to your clients so that they can gauge their progress, and to parents, relatives and possibly colleagues but also, after being qualified for a year or more, you will be expected to work with students and it will be essential for you to offer them constructive and helpful feedback.

Clinical and professionals skills

These include many of the new skills you will learn on the course that relate directly to working with the clients.

Diagnostic and therapeutic skills

Diagnostic and therapeutic skills are the basic tools of a speech and language therapist and they bring together many of the skills listed in Figure 14 above. By the time you are qualified you will be combining many of these skills, using several of them simultaneously so that you are able to work more quickly and 'think on your feet'.

For example, you will now be highly attuned to listening to people's speech in such a way that while you are attending to what they are saying you will at the same time be able to identify their speech patterns and use of linguistic structures. Usually you will be able to transcribe their speech as you listen, although you will probably be recording the session for more detailed analysis later. You will also find, for example, that you will be able to observe an interaction between two or more people, analysing aspects of the conversation as well as the non-verbal signs as you listen. At the same time you will be observing their behaviour, interpreting and drawing conclusions about what might be wrong.

As a qualified therapist you will need to gather information, to observe and analyse your observations and synthesise all the information gathered about the client, quickly putting it together with your theoretical knowledge in order to diagnose the speech and language problem.

You will then be problem-solving, drawing tentative conclusions about the nature of the problem and making informed decisions about how to proceed. As you work, particularly when carrying out therapy tasks, you will need to make spontaneous, evaluative judgements so that you are constantly adjusting and adapting your work to ensure that it is maintained at an appropriate level for the client. If your therapy isn't working you need to be aware of this and be able to change it quickly. At the end of the session you will need to talk to the parents or relatives and the clients, offering suggestions, listening to their point of view and being able to respond appropriately.

Organisational skills

Once qualified you will not only need to be able to organise yourself but also to organise your work load so that you can complete all tasks within the working week. You will need to manage your caseload so that all clients are seen, reviewed, assessed or maintained on a waiting list. You will also need to ensure that you have time for all your administration, and your own professional development.

Maintaining your skills and knowledge after qualification

When you receive your graduation certificate and become eligible to apply to the Health Professions Council (HPC) for registration as a speech and language therapist you will be a 'generalist' therapist, which means that you will be qualified to work with children and adults. Many people, however, then specialise, learning new skills, furthering their knowledge and gaining expertise in working with a specific client group.

Even if you don't choose to specialise, your education and training does not end on the day you qualify. As a health professional you have a responsibility to continue with a 'lifelong learning' programme. As you become aware of the current research that is being undertaken in speech and language therapy and related fields you will realise the importance of keeping up with new ideas and the latest findings and making sure that your therapy approach is not out-of-date.

Chapter 10 Is this career for you? How to find out more

If you are interested in becoming a speech and language therapist your first port of call should be The Royal College of Speech and Language Therapists (RCSLT).

RCSLT

RCSLT is the professional body for speech and language therapists and if you are seriously thinking about speech and language therapy and you want to find out more, then look at the RCSLT website (see *Useful Addresses*) for up-to-date information. Full membership of RCSLT provides qualified therapists with professional indemnity insurance, a monthly *Bulletin*, regular copies of the *International Journal of Language and Communication Disorders* and an up-to-date version of the professional guidelines, *Communicating Quality*. You will also gain most of these benefits by joining as a student member.

Courses and books

Some speech and language therapy departments offer open days including talks and video demonstrations and the opportunity to talk to therapists. In some Trusts it may be possible to observe a therapist at work.

There are also some establishments that offer relevant short courses such as Kings College Hospital and the City Literary Institute, in London. Further information about courses will be available through RCSLT.

You may want to look in the library for relevant books or videos about people with communication difficulties. There are many such appropriate books written by professionals in the field as well as 'first hand experience' books written by people with communication problems themselves or members of their family. There are some suggestions for such reading in the *Further Reading* section of this book.

Many applicants who are interested in communication begin to learn BSL. You would not only be learning a new language but would also be taking the opportunity to gain some insight into a different way of communicating.

Gain some practical experience

In order to find out as much as possible about people with communication difficulties take every opportunity to talk with people who have such problems. This could either be people you know – a friend, relative or neighbour, or you could visit a home for elderly people, or possibly befriend someone who has a physical impairment or learning disability.

If you are still at school it may be possible to gain some work experience with children, particularly children who have special educational needs. Or, you may wish to try for work experience in a hospital setting, in a home for elderly people, or with people with learning disabilities.

It would also be helpful to take advantage of any other experiences offered through school where you can take on a role of responsibility such as being a mentor, helping others to read, or becoming a sports captain or a prefect. It may be possible to work for a charity either as part of your work experience or on a voluntary basis outside school hours, for example Riding for the Disabled.

If you are a mature applicant you may be able to undertake some paid work, for example, as a speech and language therapy assistant or as a classroom assistant. Or you may wish to take on some relevant voluntary work in a hospital setting, a home for elderly people, or a day centre for people with learning disabilities. You could also volunteer to work in a school or a nursery, especially with children who have special educational needs.

If there is no paid work available, it may be possible to work on a voluntary basis for one of the many charities associated with people with communication disorders. For example, charities such as Mencap, The Stroke Association, Scope or Afasic are usually appreciative of such help.

You can read more about therapists working with different client groups in different settings in Part II.

Part II
Case Studies – Profiles of Speech and Language Therapists at Work in a Variety of Settings

Chapter 11 A paediatric specialist in a Child Development Centre

Susan is a paediatric speech and language therapist working with children in a Child Development Centre (CDC). She went to university straight from school and qualified as a therapist seven years ago after gaining a BSc (Hons) degree. She has had one previous job since leaving university and has been at the CDC for four years.

Although employed full time, currently she is working for only four days a week at the CDC as on the remaining day she attends the local university where she is studying for an MSc in Communication Studies. This is a part-time course spread over two years and Susan is in her second year.

She began to consider the possibility of further study during the informal lunchtime discussions that take place on specific days over coffee and sandwiches in the staff room between the available members of the multi-disciplinary team. She was stimulated by the level of discussion and realised she would like to find out more about some of the topics being discussed. Encouraged at her individual performance review by her line-manager, the Centre's senior speech and language therapist, Susan agreed to apply for the course as part of her commitment to her continuing professional development.

Since beginning the course she has been offered the opportunity to participate in some of the CDC's research relating to the effectiveness of speech and language therapy in the Centre and she has found that she has gained more confidence and is able to contribute more to the lunchtime discussions.

A ten thousand-word dissertation is required as part of the final assessment of her MSc degree and Susan is investigating parents' attitudes to their children's difficulties. This has enabled her to discuss issues in more depth than usual with the parents and she is finding that this, in turn, has been helpful when working with the children. She has really enjoyed attending lectures and seminars again. She is also gaining much through her own independent learning as it has enabled her to access up-to-the-minute research relating to the children with whom she works and has given her confidence to explore further some of the material available through the Internet.

Although Susan is enjoying the course, she does sometimes have difficulties juggling her coursework, reading and research with her clinical work – and her home life – and she is grateful not only for the support of her manger but also for the interest and support of her colleagues at the CDC. She is stimulated by their interest when she talks about the latest articles she has read, or the lectures she has attended, particularly when these are given by some leading specialist in the field. And she has also had the benefit of applying some of her new knowledge to her own assessment and therapy work. There is no doubt she is looking forward to the end of the course in September when she will have more time for her friends and family but she hopes the course will have stimulated her to continue with her professional development in other ways.

Susan loves the working atmosphere in the CDC where the multi-disciplinary team functions smoothly and the members each respect the others' expertise. She also likes the fact that each day is different depending on which consultants are holding their clinics. For example, on Mondays, Susan starts the day running a clinic jointly with one of the paediatricians and the Centre's clinical psychologist. GPs normally refer children to the CDC if they have concerns about any child's development generally, and speech and language development in particular, and such children would usually be seen during this Monday morning clinic.

Sometimes the team are able to see a number of children during the morning if they are attending for a follow-up or review session having been previously assessed. On other occasions the whole morning may be taken up with a child being seen for an initial multi-disciplinary assessment as this takes a considerable amount of time.

Susan carries out the communication assessment for each child. Usually, when the parents attend with the child, she is then able to involve them in the assessment. They can sometimes help if the child is uncooperative and they can tell her how typical the child's performance and behaviour is in relation to their conduct at home.

Susan uses a variety of books, toys and games, as well as specifically devised assessments, to help her find out about different aspects of the child's communication skills and she will check with the parents about the child's speech and language history as well as their ability to communicate outside the clinic. She needs to know how the child communicates with different people and in different situations. She needs to observe whether their speech is clear and whether their language, and the way in which they communicate, is appropriate for their age. When the parents are there, Susan can often learn much by carefully observing them playing and interacting with the child.

After the initial assessments the multi-disciplinary team members meet to discuss their assessment findings and, where possible, to agree the diagnosis. They then decide on the information that will be most helpful to give to the family before they meet with them. An integrated, holistic management plan that will best help the child can then be agreed.

As the CDC is regarded as a Centre of Excellence staffed by some of the top specialists in their field, children may attend for assessment from a wide geographic area. Sometimes, therefore, if speech and language therapy is needed, it might be recommended that this is carried out by a therapist located closer to the child's home and Susan will then liaise with that therapist and discuss the CDC team's findings and recommendations.

Occasionally if the child has already been seen by the

local therapist then s/he may attend the CDC assessment together with the parents. This therapist may then be involved in the discussions and be able to provide additional information to be taken into account in the recommendations for the child's future management.

Susan specialises in working with children with autistic spectrum disorder and complex disabilities including feeding problems. As 80% of the referrals to the joint speech and language therapy assessment clinics involve children with possible autistic spectrum disorders Susan was sent on a specialist training course for assessment and diagnosis and sometimes she will see these children herself for therapy.

During these sessions she will be able to demonstrate activities to the parents, for them to continue at home. Where necessary, Susan will liaise with other professionals who are involved with the child such as a physiotherapist or an occupational therapist, a dietician, or an outreach nurse.

After the Monday morning clinic Susan spends most of the lunch hour at the nursery situated next door. Here she works with Heather one of the nursery nurses helping Colin, a three year old with cerebral palsy, to eat his lunch. Colin has dysphagia and his eating and swallowing cause concern among the nursery staff. They were reluctant for him to stay for lunch because it was taking him so long to eat his food and because he so often seemed to be choking. Susan offered to show the staff strategies for feeding that would prevent him choking and they all agree that thanks to Susan's help they are now more confident about Colin eating at the nursery.

On Monday afternoons, Susan has been making home visits to Sarah, a two and a half year old who has Down Syndrome and who is learning to communicate through Makaton signs. This is a signing system based on BSL and Susan has picked out some simple key words for Sarah's mother to sign.

For example, Sarah loves going out and so Susan concentrated on what she noticed were constantly used phrases: 'Shall we go out now', 'To the shops', 'To the park', 'Let's get your coat from the cupboard'. She picked out the key words 'go', 'shops', 'park' and 'coat' and showed Sarah's mother how to sign the words as she speaks the longer phrases.

Although Susan is confident that Sarah will be able to speak eventually, she has encouraged Sarah's mother and her grandmother who lives with them to use these signs while they are speaking, to help Sarah to communicate now. She explained that by using the signs they are also helping Sarah to understand, as well as giving her a means to express herself, and Susan suggests more key words each time she goes. Susan has arranged with Sarah's mother that she will visit the playgroup to give advice to the staff about Sarah's communication and to teach them some Makaton signs.

Both Mum and Granny are now enthusiastic Makaton signers. They have told Susan that Sarah now signs back to them and that she doesn't seem to be so frustrated as she can usually make her needs known.

By four o'clock in the afternoon, traffic permitting, Susan is back at the CDC where, on most Mondays, she meets with one of her speech and language therapy colleagues. They are responsible for running in-service training days (Inset days) for staff at three of the local primary schools. This gives them the opportunity to show teachers, who have not necessarily had any specialist training about children with speech and language problems, how to recognise some of the more typical problems they might find in the children in their mainstream classes.

During such sessions they try to help the teachers and LSAs to understand the effects such problems might have on the children's school work. They try to encourage them to refer children who may need help to speech and language therapy. They also suggest ideas for simple tasks that might be helpful within the classroom, particularly for developing children's language skills. In order to make such sessions as interesting as possible for the staff, Susan and her colleague need to prepare well and this takes much thought and careful planning. They have found that they have learned a great deal from working with the teachers and LSAs in this way.

In the mornings on Tuesdays and Wednesdays, Susan works in different specialist clinics and sometimes has a student with her. One of these clinics is run by the consultant paediatric neurologist and most of the children are referred because of a concern that they may have epilepsy. In the other clinic Susan works with one of the consultant paediatricians with children who have been diagnosed at birth as having multiple medical and cognitive problems. These children may have a recognised – and often rare – syndrome, they may have cerebral palsy, or the cause of their problems may be unknown. Many of these children will show evidence of severe learning disabilities.

Working in both of these clinics is very demanding as each of the children has very different and usually complex problems, and it is Susan's job to consider all aspects of their communication and eating and drinking difficulties. She has to think about not only the implications of these problems on their general development but also the implications of their medical problems on the development of their speech, language and communication skills.

On Tuesdays and Wednesdays Susan usually tries to eat her sandwiches at lunchtime in the staff room as it is then that the most interesting staff discussions are held. The afternoons are used for seeing children for individual or small group therapy sessions. Sometimes she will work with children who have been referred from the nursery next door to the CDC. At other times she will have an appointment to see a child for therapy following an assessment.

On Thursdays Susan attends university, a full day of lectures, seminars and tutorials and so by Friday she is very pleased to have some time set aside to catch up on her administrative tasks. This is the time to return phone calls; to make calls checking with other therapists about specific children; to write her contribution to joint clinic reports; to prepare sessions; to read new referrals; to send out appointments and to write letters. It is also a time when she can work on the CDC research in which she has been involved; when multi-disciplinary team meetings are held; when preparations are made for the following week's clinics, and of course to deal with any emergencies. If she has a spare moment, the staff in the nursery always appreciates her popping in and offering any help and advice.

By Friday night she is ready for the weekend – although until her course is over she will have to spend some part of that writing essays and coursework and preparing for her final exams.

Susan became a speech and language therapist because she liked the variety the job offered and she has not been disappointed because she rarely seems to be doing the same thing twice. Progress for many of the children with whom she works is slow and often limited. However, she monitors and evaluates progress as she works with the children so that she knows that the therapy is making a difference.

Perhaps what has surprised her most is how much she has enjoyed returning to study and how glad she is she didn't take her own advice after completing her last exam on her undergraduate speech and language therapy course when she vowed 'never again'!

Chapter 12 A specialist working with adults in an acute hospital

David left school after he had successfully completed his 'A' levels. He had already secured a place on a speech and language therapy course but decided to have a gap year so that he could travel to see parts of the world he had always wanted to visit. He thought it would be useful to experience first hand how it felt being in different countries where he didn't know one word of the language. For the remainder of the year on his return, he wanted to spend time working with different groups of people with communication difficulties.

He first heard about speech and language therapy when he was in his teens and his grandmother had a stroke. He couldn't work out why she seemed able to understand most of what he and the rest of the family said but was not able to say more than a few inappropriate sentences herself. He met the speech and language therapist who came once a week to see her privately at his Gran's home and was fascinated watching her work.

After watching – and helping – his Gran regain much of her speech he volunteered to help at a stroke club. After that, he volunteered to be a 'friend' to people with learning disabilities who were living in a local hostel and he also worked at a community club for deaf people. Observing speech and language therapists working in different settings helped to confirm his earlier decision and he applied to train as a speech and language therapist.

Despite the warnings, he did find it strange at first when he started his undergraduate course because he was the only man amongst thirty woman students, and most of those had come straight from school. But he soon made friends and once he began clinical work found he didn't think about it any more.

When he qualified, his first job allowed him to work

with adults and with children, but then he decided he definitely preferred working with adults and changed jobs so that he could specialise in acquired disorders.

He has been in his current job in the speech and language therapy department in an acute hospital for five years. There are three other speech and language therapists in the department one of whom is his assigned mentor and they are managed by a senior speech and language therapist also based there. David has regular meetings with his mentor to discuss the patients.

The speech and language therapists and the physiotherapists share office space in the new wing of the hospital and sometimes they see patients together in one of the clinic rooms. David also uses the clinic rooms to see individual patients, although much of his work is done on the wards.

Most of the patients that he sees have lost their communication skills suddenly – even dramatically – as the result of a stroke or because of a head injury following a road traffic accident. They are usually very ill when they are first admitted to the hospital and that's when David first sees them on the ward. Some of the patients recover their speech and language spontaneously without any help, or with just a little help from David or his colleagues. But others need much work and support while they are in hospital and continue to do so when they leave.

David sees patients individually one morning and three afternoons a week. The rest of the time he spends on the wards assessing or conducting therapy sessions; carrying out in-service training, or in meetings. Meetings are an important part of his work as, for example, he often needs to get together with the ward staff to discuss the patients' progress. He also needs to meet with his own speech and language therapy colleagues in the department so that they can evaluate their work and ensure that they are meeting their required targets by seeing people within the time limit recommended by the RCSLT and specified by their Trust.

Every Thursday a final year undergraduate speech and language therapy student from the nearby university comes to work with David. He enjoys this. He enjoys watching the student progress and develop. The student, in turn, is often able to bring him some 'hot off the press' information about an assessment or a procedure that he doesn't yet know about. He gives the student as much opportunity as possible to work independently but he always plans ahead each week to make sure that there is time for feedback and discussion at the end of the day.

The first thing they both do on Thursday mornings is attend the ward round in the hospital. This is led by a consultant neurologist, accompanied by other members of the medical team, the speech and language therapists and physiotherapists as well as by representatives of the nursing staff. David finds that these are wonderful opportunities to share information with colleagues, but he knows his student does not relax, worrying that the consultant will ask her a question she'll find difficult to answer.

There are three people on Byron, a mixed ward with male and female patients, that David has been working with and he is keen to hear the views of the other members of the team about their condition. He is pleased with the progress made by Eileen Jones, a sixty five year old retired secretary, who was admitted following a stroke and he wonders if she might be ready soon for discharge.

When he first assessed Eileen, she had very little speech although she was able to understand. Although David wasn't sure at first about her prognosis, she had in fact made much spontaneous recovery without his help. He is now hopeful that a short period of individual therapy will help her to make even more progress. He will make sure she has some strategies for dealing with any awkward moments when she might have difficulties finding the right word, and it is possible that she might be able to talk almost as well as she did before her stroke by the time she is ready for discharge.

David is more concerned about Billy Brown. Billy has also had a stroke, although he is only forty years old, but he is not making as much progress as David had first hoped. He seems to have limited understanding and appears uninterested in what is going on around him, not even showing any interest when he was visited by his young family.

He also has the added complication of severe swallowing problems. The physiotherapist is pleased with the way Billy is regaining some movement in his right arm and leg, which was completely paralysed at the time of the stroke, but she too is concerned about his low spirits.

The possibility of Billy being referred to a rehabilitation centre has been discussed but the consultant is hoping that David will be able to make some progress with the swallowing difficulties before the final decision is made. David made a referral for Billy to have a videofluoroscopy examination as soon as there were signs of sufficient physical and medical improvement and he is now awaiting the results from his manager with recommendations for further therapy.

The third patient Ramesh Patel, a lively seventy year old, is awaiting confirmation from the consultant of his discharge, as the nursing staff and the occupational therapist feel he is fit enough to go home. They have asked social services to organise the appropriate support for him and his family. He will return as an outpatient for further speech and language therapy, to help him organise his speech into coherent sentences and to support him with his reading which has also been affected by the stroke.

David needs to discuss with Mr Patel's family about continuing his treatment for a few weeks and he will return after the ward round to arrange an outpatient appointment for him. David hopes that the family might be able to bring him in by car so that he will not have to worry about organising ambulance transport.

After last week's ward round David observed the student carrying out a bedside communication assessment on another new patient who was not well enough to come down to the department. He was impressed by the way she talked to the patient and handled the pictures and objects that were part of the standardised procedure which the patient had difficulty managing. He does not observe her every week as she is already working like a newly qualified therapist, but he likes to check from time to time that she is able to pull all the information together quickly, and that she is integrating the relevant theory into her clinical practice.

David needs to ensure that when the student's university tutor visits to discuss the student's progress she will be as pleased as he is about the student's professional development. David will miss the student when she finishes at the end of the spring term as she has responded well to his feedback.

Much to his surprise he has found that he enjoys teaching. He has also enjoyed the lecturing that he has been asked to do recently. He has been teaching post-graduate nurses about communication problems associated with strokes and he was pleased to be able to involve the student in the practical workshop he agreed to run after the talk.

David always enjoyed the neurological side of his studies while at university and what he particularly enjoys about his current job is that the work enables him to continue to develop this specialist aspect. On several occasions he has been able to attend post-qualification short courses specifically related to the neurological aspects of his work, and he has continued to develop the depth and breadth of his knowledge and skills in this area. To keep himself up-to-date he reads as much as possible about the latest research particularly relating to that area, and at four o'clock every Friday afternoon he joins the other members of the neurological team to attend a 'journal group' where interested hospital staff discuss a specific journal article.

Other members of the speech and language therapy department are currently involved with the team in neurological research and David has begun to consider the possibility of applying for a Master's course in cognitive- or neuro-psychology.

Chapter 13 A paediatric therapist working in mainstream schools

Amita is a member of the speech and language therapy team that works in mainstream schools in an inner city area, close to where she lives. Although like most speech and language therapists she is employed by the NHS, she spends all her working time in schools. When she was at university she particularly enjoyed one of her ongoing placements when she worked for one day each week with her supervising clinician and other speech and language therapists as part of their school team.

On graduation two years ago, she was delighted to find a job where she would also be part of a school team. One day she hopes to manage such a team but at the moment she is working on developing the clinical and collaborative skills that will help her work most effectively with the children.

Although she spends all day working with the children within the schools, Amita's base is in one of the local health centres where she shares a room with several others in her team. Here she keeps her files, has the use of a phone and computer and can usually find some desk space when she returns there at the end of each day to catch up on her paperwork and phone calls. She goes to the health centre to catch up on her administrative work. This involves writing letters and reports, contacting parents, making any necessary appointments and filling out the forms of client-related statistics. She sometimes has support from a secretary, or assistant, to prepare programmes and activities.

Like each of the members of the schools speech and language therapy team she is responsible for several specific schools and she has spent much of the last two years getting to know the children and building good working relationships with the schools' staff. In all but one of the schools she has managed this, remembering from her student days the importance of ensuring she had strong links with the head teacher, the SENCo and the school secretary. Only in one school does she feel she still has a lot of work to do in order not to feel like the 'visitor' she knows she is.

In all the other schools she has found that the positive reception from the head teacher has helped her forge good working relations with the rest of the staff even though she doesn't necessarily see the head each time she goes into the school. Usually it is the SENCo who is her first port of call and in most of her schools they often meet in the staff room over an early morning coffee. There, the SENCo brings Amita up-to-date on the children she is already working with and Amita hears about any other children she needs to follow up.

In most of Amita's schools it is the SENCo who has been able to ensure that the speech and language therapy work is incorporated into relevant teaching plans and integrated into regular classroom activities and Amita has found that in most instances she has been able to develop a close working relationship with the SENCos.

Establishing a good relationship with the school secretary has also stood Amita in good stead, for she has found it is usually the secretary who knows which staff are available and who is off sick.

Amita usually works with the children in the classroom, occasionally withdrawing them for individual work. When Amita is working within the classroom she is aware of the topics and themes they are working on in class and is able to make all her speech and language therapy work relevant to the National Curriculum.

She agrees in advance with the teacher the role she will take with the child she is working with. Sometimes they agree it is best for her to sit beside the child so that when the teacher has introduced the topic Amita will then try to find out how much the child can do alone or whether he/she needs prompting or a helping hand.

Or, Amita may sit together with the child and the LSA, offering individual suggestions and support while the teacher is working with the class as a whole. After the lesson she will then be able to suggest to the LSA ways in which this support may be continued so that it will be most beneficial to the child's speech and language development.

Sometimes working in the classroom means sitting in a quiet corner with the child, working individually on a specific topic while the rest of the class are getting on with other work.

At the beginning of the school year Amita was asked to see six-year-old girl Bahar who originally came from Turkey. The teacher was concerned with her speech and language development. It had already been established that Bahar had difficulties in both of her languages so that it is not just a question of her not yet having learned English.

Amita is now hoping to meet with Bahar's mother. However, as she only speaks Turkish, Amita has asked for a bilingual co-worker to join them. She hopes she will be able to find out more about how Bahar communicates at home.

Many of the children Amita sees have a Statement of Special Educational Need – the legally binding document that records the child's needs, including speech and language therapy, and the ways in which they will be provided for. Often a Statement will result in a learning support assistant – who is answerable to the SENCo – being assigned to work with a specific child. Amita usually works with statemented children on a regular basis, asking the assistants to continue with some of the speech and language therapy tasks and activities on the days when she herself is not in the school. She finds that they usually enjoy this work and are able to contribute many creative ideas and materials that can be used to carry out the activities.

Amita has a number of children that she is responsible

for in each school and if the school is supportive she is often able to work with children who have speech and language problems but who don't have a Statement. Usually she will work closely with the assistant, demonstrating the speech and language therapy work for the assistant to carry out later.

In fact, when she first began working in schools, Amita was surprised how much of her time was spent training other staff, particularly the assistants. She has since been asked to run training workshops for the teachers, volunteers and occasionally parents. Although she felt nervous about running such workshops at first, she finds she now really enjoys this part of the job.

Recently she was asked by the head of one school to run an after-hours session for the teachers and LSAs in that school. The session comprised working on recognising comprehension problems in children, looking at how the staff might help the children who didn't seem to be following instructions properly or understanding the work they were doing in class. Although it was an informal session and not part of the teachers' compulsory in-service training, a large number of staff attended voluntarily. This was partly because they are committed to their work with the children, but partly because they enjoy working with Amita. Amita worked hard to make the topic interesting and was pleased that they seemed to enjoy the session as well.

Amita likes being peripatetic and going to a different school each day, particularly now that she has established herself in most of the schools. What she doesn't like is having to move at lunchtime. Not only does she find it difficult to find a place to eat her sandwiches in peace, but also she loses the opportunity to talk to the staff; loses the chance to exchange information or to explain more about speech and language therapy. This can often be the only time she gets to meet some of the teachers whose timetables are full, so usually she will try to ensure she has at least a half hour lunch break when she can chat informally in the staff room.

During any one week Amita might have to attend two or even three annual review meetings for children with Statements, usually at different schools. Here she will meet with the parents of the children and all the other professionals who support the individual child such as the head teacher, the SENCo, the class teacher and, in some instances, a specialist teacher, an educational psychologist and possibly a social worker. When she was first qualified Amita felt daunted by the size of such a group and she often wonders how the children's parents feel when confronted by so many people. But now she is used to explaining her approach to large groups of people from different professional backgrounds and finds the reviews very informative.

Amita first decided she wanted to become a speech and language therapist when she found out the subjects she would be studying if she took the university course. She was good at school at both science and arts subjects but could not find many university courses that would allow her to study such a combination.

She had thought of becoming a doctor but hated giving up her arts subjects. When she found out about the amount of client contact enjoyed by speech and language therapists she realised this was the career for her. Her parents on the other hand were not initially happy about her choice. Speech and language therapy was not something they had heard of and they would have preferred their only daughter to become a doctor. Now, however, Amita knows that they are very proud of her work.

Chapter 14 A specialist working with people who stammer

Penny went to study on a speech and language therapy course straight from school and has now been qualified for eight years. During that time she has worked in several different speech and language therapy jobs as the family has moved around the country with her husband's company. She has worked with children in schools and health centres in an inner city area, and with adults in a more remote rural area where she spent much of her time working with elderly people in residential settings.

Over the years she has found she's enjoyed working with children and adults, and would really have liked to work with both groups at the same time so she didn't think about specialising in any particular area as that usually involves having to choose between children or adults. However, when she first settled in the small town where she now lives, the speech and language therapy manager in the department where she works was keen for someone to develop a more specialist role in working with people who stammer.

Remembering a particularly enjoyable student placement in a specialist stammering clinic Penny expressed an interest. She had also enjoyed working during her gap year in the USA in a specialist centre for people who stutter – as they usually refer to stammering over there. She began to read round the subject again so that she was familiar with the latest research and approaches to stammering; she attended a special course for clinicians to update her skills, and signed up to attend the international conference held in Oxford.

At first she only had one or two children on her caseload who stammered but soon, as she learned more and her name became known locally, she found herself dealing solely with people who stammer, people of all ages, from all around the area as they were referred to her through schools, GPs, and parents.

She found she loved the work and is continuing to develop her special expertise.

Now Penny spends most of her week seeing children and adults who are disfluent or who stammer. Some of the people she sees have a severe stammer that makes communication very difficult and emotionally draining. Others stammer less often but have developed coping strategies, such as avoiding words and situations, which hold them back in school and at work.

One of the things Penny enjoys about her work is the variety of people she works with such as Rita, a local councillor, who stammers when she has to make speeches and is working on making more effective public presentations; or Gary who doesn't stammer when he's singing in the school choir but is afraid to answer questions in class, and Rachel who mostly doesn't seem to be bothered by her stammer but has asked for strategies to help her on the odd occasions when she does block on a word and suddenly finds herself unable to utter a sound. Penny enjoys the feelings of satisfaction that she and her clients experience as they gain confidence when she is able to help them to speak more easily and tackle situations they previously found difficult.

In order to be accessible to clients from all over the area, Penny now spends part of the week based in a community clinic where she sees children. She sees the adults at the main hospital and she also runs an evening group at a local Further Education college. Since starting to work in this specialised area she has become particularly interested in working with adults and has thought she would like to specialise in working only with adults some day. But that might need to wait for another move.

In the meantime she has had two new young children referred to her at the community clinic by one of the local health visitors. Jamie is three and half and Tom is rising five and about to start school. In both cases their parents have expressed concern about their child's fluency.

Penny will see them individually, with one or preferably both of their parents. The initial assessment session for all children who are thought to be stammering normally takes at least two hours and Penny stressed this to the parents over the phone when she made the appointments so that they can make appropriate arrangements for their other children.

During the assessment Penny will watch the parents playing with their children and video the session for later analysis and discussion with them. She will also ask the parents detailed questions about their child's development and establish how the child functions within the family. She will carry out the discussion with the parents without the child in the room. This may mean that two appointments have to be arranged.

She will obviously have to spend some time looking at each of the children themselves in order to assess their levels of understanding as well as the ways in which they express themselves. Because Jamie is so young, Penny is wondering how much he is 'at risk' of continuing to stammer as most children recover from early stammering without any therapy. The health visitor has stressed that Jamie himself is not upset by his disfluent speech but, as the parents are worried, Penny is keen to see them as soon as possible. With the right kind of advice at the right time she may be able to prevent Jamie from continuing to stammer.

She has more concerns about Tom as he is about to go to school and according to the health visitor not only are the parents worried but Tom himself gets distressed when he cannot get his words out. Penny sent his parents a questionnaire to complete before they came so that she would have more time for discussion during her session with them. When they returned it by post as requested she was not surprised to find that Tom's father and his grandfather both stammer. This is not unusual and will help Penny when she is making decisions about the kind of help and advice Tom and his parents will need. She would hope that with Tom's and his parents' cooperation they might see some encouraging results, although of course there can be no guarantees.

In line with her local authority policy, if Penny feels it necessary she will be able to offer Tom up to six weeks of therapy and this can be repeated several times. Then he would have a break for a few months before he would be reviewed and seen again if necessary. In addition to any therapy, Penny normally gives parents information about the British Stammering Association that can often provide ongoing support.

Once she has completed the assessments, Penny will write a report on each child. She types her own reports on the word processor in the clinic as she does not have a secretary and she will send a copy to the parents, to the health visitor and to any other professional such as the audiologist if she feels they need to become involved.

Although most of her working days are filled by seeing clients and their families, Penny does try to leave some time, usually at the end of the week, to make phone calls, to organise her sessions for the following week, and to attend meetings. For example, she has been helping to test a new disfluency programme and she needs to meet with other therapists who have also been using it to discuss its effectiveness. One of the places Penny meets other therapists who share her specialised interest is the Special Interest Group (SIG) of the RCSLT. At their quarterly meetings they invite specialist speakers. They also have an opportunity to share their own ideas and knowledge, and Penny has become an active member. She is also a member of the British Stammering Association and finds their website and regular magazine invaluable.

She has presented some of her own work at the international conference as well as presenting a paper at the recent RCSLT conference that has now been published. At first she found such presentations daunting, but she persevered knowing that it is important for her to share her work if she is to establish herself as an expert in the field.

She is beginning to gain some recognition. Recently she was invited by the local university to give some lectures about her work and to run a workshop for the third year students on a speech and language therapy course.

As well as teaching others Penny herself continues to learn. She attends courses for example, to learn about new techniques and the latest programmes that come on the market from as far afield as the USA or Australia, as well as from within the UK. She feels she needs to be able to give her clients a balanced and unbiased opinion about what might be helpful to their specific problem, because she knows that stammering has various and complex causes, in many cases being associated with other speech and language problems. She also knows that in the long term there are no 'miracle cures' and, because of the diverse nature of stammering, there is not one method or technique that suits everyone as therapy.

Before Penny decided to become a speech and language therapist she had thought she would like to be a teacher. She chose therapy because she thought she was more suited to working with people one-to-one. One of the surprises for Penny since she has been working as a speech and language therapist is how much of her work involves working with groups. Now she runs groups for much of the time and even runs small classes in the Further Education centre. She finds her work extremely challenging but rewarding and she has no regrets that she chose to become a speech and language therapist, nor any regrets about her chosen area of specialisation.

Chapter 15 Working in a special school

Andrew qualified as a speech and language therapist ten years ago and now works as a senior therapist in a special school for children from three to nineteen years who have severe physical and learning disabilities. He manages the two other speech and language therapists who work part-time there, one in the senior end of the school and the other who is based in the nursery department, and a speech and language therapy assistant. In his role as line-manager he meets with them on a monthly basis so that they can discuss their work and plan future activities, although he encourages them to talk to him at any time as problems or special discussion points arise.

Andrew has recently attended a two day advanced course about eating, drinking and swallowing problems. He tries to attend such courses every two or three years so that he can add to the knowledge he brought with him from his original training. When attending such courses Andrew always appreciates the opportunity to talk with colleagues involved in similar work in schools around the country. This time he heard about a therapist in another area who was working in a school in less than ideal conditions. It made him appreciate the fact that in the school where he works the staff generously share their time and expertise with each other. On Friday, at the regular staff meeting, he will have the opportunity to share with his colleagues information from the swallowing course.

Whenever Andrew has been away from school for any length of time, he likes to come in early on the first morning back so that he can catch up with his post and phone messages before starting the first session with the children. He always looks forward to seeing the children again and is gratified to find that they have usually missed him.

Ben is one of those children. He is an eight-year-old who has cerebral palsy, which in his case means he is confined to a wheelchair and has limited use of his arms. He cannot speak but makes his personality known through grunting noises and deep-throated laughter. He communicates using an electronic communication aid that produces a computerised voice speaking a variety of words and phrases when different areas of the touch screen are pressed.

However, because his hand movements are limited, it is not easy for Ben to apply enough pressure to the relevant areas on the aid in order to activate the voice appropriately. At the moment he hits it with the palm of his hand but this is not accurate enough and he is often frustrated if the wrong words are activated. As Ben has more control of his head than his hand movements, Andrew and the occupational therapist have decided that Ben might manage better with a switch on the headrest of his wheelchair that he will press with the side of his head to activate the communication aid and indicate what he wants to say. Andrew has been working with the school technician, trying to find the most effective way for Ben to make contact with the aid and they will be soon be putting this one to the test.

Most of the children with whom Andrew works have such severe problems that he often sees them jointly with the physiotherapist. Some of the children are able to speak and to help them do this they need to be able to draw the maximum amount of air into their lungs. They need to have as clear an airway as possible if they are to co-ordinate their breathing with vocalisation, sound making, and ultimately speech. When Andrew is using this co-ordinated approach, the physiotherapist helps to position the children and to ensure that they can maintain the best possible posture to enable speech.

Working in a co-ordinated way like this means that the maximum use is made of the professionals' time in the school. As most of the children are brought to school by special transport they don't arrive until well after nine in the morning and have to be ready for their transport home by three in the afternoon. There are not many hours in between, therefore, to complete all the work required during the school day.

At least once a month there is an annual review held on one of the children within the school. The next one will be about Deepak. Fortunately Andrew wrote his report for the review two weeks ago, before he went on the course, so he does not have to worry now about the time pressure since his return. He is anticipating that it will be a difficult meeting because Deepak's parents are disappointed that their son has not made more progress with the communication aid he received last term.

Andrew knows that it has taken Deepak longer than anyone expected to become familiar with the aid. He has been using it if he needs to ask for something in class but has not been using it to help him take part in lessons. Andrew acknowledges that it does take time to become comfortable about using an aid and to become familiar with it. He feels that some changes will need to be made within the classroom environment in order to encourage Deepak to use his aid fully. Andrew will, therefore, suggest some new strategies that could be tried in the classroom. He has already discussed his ideas with the class teacher and he knows he has her support and the support of the assistant who is willing to try out his ideas. Andrew has also discussed with the physiotherapist some suggestions they wish to make jointly to the parents in the hope that they will be willing to test out some new strategies at home.

Once a week Andrew joins the reception class in the Snoozeland room that has been specially designed for people who need a great deal of sensory stimulation within a safe environment. It is a well-lit room and all the equipment, which is bright and visually attractive, is made from tactile materials and fabrics to try to stimulate a response from children with profound learning disabilities. It has been specifically designed and created so that all the pieces of equipment are soft and free from sharp edges, forming a completely safe environment for the children.

Such rooms are expensive to create, however, and this one has been developed over the last four years through fundraising activities within the school. But the efforts of the staff and the children have proved worthwhile, for there is no doubt that some of the children in the school with the most severe problems have benefited from working with the equipment. Andrew enjoys the sessions he carries out there and feels rewarded when he sees a child who is normally silent and unable to move reach out towards one of the mobiles and begin to make sounds indicating the child's interest.

One of Andrew's duties is to see some children at home before they begin attending the school. Tomorrow morning he will go with the SENCo on such a visit. Robbie will be coming to the school shortly and Andrew and the SENCo hope the visit will help them begin to build links with the parents before the new term starts. Seeing Robbie within his home environment will also help to give Andrew a more rounded picture of his communication. This is true of most children, particularly those who have severe physical problems and limited communication skills.

Robbie's family is new to the area. Although the files haven't yet arrived from the previous therapist, a letter and brief report have informed Andrew that eight year old Robbie is not able to walk and has his own wheelchair. He is able to talk and is reported to be working at a level that is appropriate for his age. However, he has a progressive condition which means that his muscles are gradually wasting and he needs much medical support. It was felt he would be able to receive this more comfortably in a special school than in a local mainstream primary school. Andrew hopes to be able to help Robbie maintain his speech and language for as long as possible and is looking forward to working with him.

After the visit and on three afternoons a week Andrew helps the teacher and the LSA run the social skills and social communication group for the school leavers. These are the older students who will soon be moving on, mostly to semi-independent living in hostels or small residential settings. Some will go on to attend classes at a Further Education college. Others will begin work, some in sheltered workshops, depending on their abilities. Within the group the leavers learn strategies to help them communicate, to manage transport systems where necessary, and learn how to cope generally with the wider world beyond school.

For Andrew the work within the school is full of variety and he enjoys all the different aspects. He likes working with the pupils and the fact that he can collaborate closely with his colleagues. However, he especially enjoys working with the technical aids technician when he can use all his own computing skills.

Andrew first heard about speech and language therapy from a careers leaflet. Before that, he had been considering a career in computing but preferred the idea of human communication. However, he realised when he began working in the school shortly after qualifying that here he would be able to combine the two and is delighted to have found what he considers to be his specialist niche. He is extremely interested in working with and developing electronic communication aids and spends much time after school with the technician trying to solve technical problems for the children. He is hoping to continue to develop these skills.

Chapter 16 A peripatetic therapist working in a rural area

Moira works as a peripatetic speech and language therapist in a rural area travelling between the different schools for which she is responsible. This means that she spends a lot of time in the car and eats many of her packed sandwich lunches in a country lay-by between sessions!

Moira has always enjoyed the autonomy that a career in speech and language therapy offers her but she is now enjoying even more autonomy than she had previously. She likes being able to control her own timetable and, in this job, she has to plan each day carefully in order to make best use of her time, working efficiently with maximum effect.

She has sole responsibility for a large geographic rural area and is responsible for dealing with all the school-aged children with speech and language problems within that area, seeing the children within their schools. However, as there are so many schools to be covered Moira is unable to carry out all of the work herself with the individual children and often has to work indirectly. This usually means that together with the teachers she devises a speech and language therapy programme for each child which is then carried out by the LSA. Moira follows up the work and reviews the children's progress with the LSAs later in the term.

When Moira first began this job her main concern was one of isolation. In her previous jobs she had been based either in a hospital or a clinic where other speech and language therapists worked, and there was always someone with whom she could discuss any difficult problems. But, when her family had to relocate after her husband was made redundant, she had to find a job in a more rural area, far removed from their former home. Moira decided this was her opportunity to apply for a different type of speech and language therapy post.

She is a very experienced therapist having worked in a variety of jobs for the last twenty four years. She had two career breaks when her children were small but always returned to speech and language therapy as she enjoyed the work so much. The speech and language therapy manager in the area where Moira now works was delighted to have someone with Moira's experience joining her team.

Moira has found that working in a rural setting is very different from her previous work but she feels more settled now that she is getting to know the area. She makes good use of email, and sends texts as well as calling from the mobile phone that has been provided by the service. In this way she can keep in touch with her manager and distant colleagues and make contact with the schools.

She looks forward to the six-monthly meetings of all the speech and language therapists in the area. Then she can catch up with what others are doing and exchange views and information. After the meetings several of the therapists go out socially for a meal together and Moira likes to join them as it helps them to bond as a team. The team of paediatric therapists meets once every three months to discuss the approaches they are taking with specific children. Moira finds these meetings very relevant to her work and she has offered to talk about some of the children she is working with at the next meeting.

She is working in one of the schools with a little boy who has Landau Kleffner syndrome. Carl developed normally until he was three years old and then, following a series of seizures, began to lose his speech and language until now he sometimes doesn't even answer to his name. As it is such a rare syndrome he was diagnosed at one of the major hospitals in London, although he has now been referred back to Moira for therapy as he lives in the area. He is a challenging little boy and she is in touch with the therapist in the team who carried out his initial assessment at the Child Development Centre. They are keen to mark his progress and next time they review him Moira will go with him to discuss this with the London team. Moira has also found her membership of the RCSLT Special Interest Group helpful when working with Carl, as she is able to gain further ideas about how to help him.

When she started working in the area, one of her colleagues was working in a health centre that had a very poor record for speech and language therapy attendance despite the fact that there was a long waiting list. The therapist there found it frustrating when people did not attend appointments as it wasted so much of her time. In order to overcome this problem, she discussed it Moira and the local health visitors. They made her aware of the level of socio-economic difficulties faced by so many of the families in the area. As many of the children on the waiting list were attending a nursery class that Moira was visiting she offered to meet with the nursery teacher to discuss the possibility of her seeing the children within the nursery. The teacher was very co-operative and the other therapist was pleased that Moira was able to help in this way. This innovation has proved to be an effective way of working with the children particularly as the nursery staff are keen to carry on Moira's work when she is not there.

Moira also has the added bonus of being able to talk to the parents when they collect their children at the end of the day. Perhaps even more surprising – and pleasing for Moira – was the number of parents who attended the parents' evening at the end of last term. There she was able to speak to the parents of most of the children she sees within the nursery class. Moira's speech and language therapy manager is delighted that Moira was able to use her experience to think laterally and solve the potential problem for children in the area in a different, practical and satisfactory way.

As with all full-time therapists, Moira's week is divided

into ten sessions. These are divided between the schools for which she is responsible. At the end of each day she uses a room in a community clinic to carry out her administrative work.

During the summer holidays Moira gets together with two other therapists from nearby areas to run language and speech groups for many of the school-aged children. She is also involved in carrying out assessments to reduce waiting lists at some of the community clinics. She usually takes her own holidays during this time so that she is always available to work with the children during term time.

When Moira was still at school she heard a careers talk about occupational therapy, physiotherapy and speech and language therapy and decided that speech and language therapy appealed most to her areas of interest.

She has always felt that she made the right career choice as speech and language therapy has proved to be ideal for her. She has found the work to be so varied and always stimulating. Moira thought she would only want to work with adults when she first qualified but she has now found she really enjoys working with children. Speech and language therapy has enabled Moira to take career breaks and return to work without any difficulty. During one of her breaks she took some courses which were part of a psychology degree with the Open University. These were not only interesting but proved helpful when she returned to work.

Chapter 17 A newly qualified therapist in a split post

Kirsty studied for a degree in geography as it had been her favourite subject in school and was pleased when she got a 2:1 classification at the end of her studies. But she didn't know what she wanted to do with her degree even after she left university. She had always had a vague notion about 'wanting to help people' and while she was at university she volunteered to work on 'Nightline', the student telephone support service, and acted as a mentor for children in a local primary school. During a couple of the long summer breaks while she was studying she also spent time acting as a 'counselor' at Camp America where she worked with teenagers, before embarking on a Greyhound bus package to travel across the USA as a tourist.

She had not taken a gap year before starting university and so, once she gained her degree, she decided to continue broadening her experience by joining VSO. All these invaluable experiences in the voluntary sector convinced Kirsty that ultimately she wanted to work with people, preferably in one of the 'helping' professions. But it was not until her return when she volunteered to work at the charity Mencap, in one of the clubs they run for people with severe learning disabilities, that she heard about speech and language therapy.

She thought it sounded interesting and she went on the Internet where she found the RCSLT website and other sources of information. The more she read about it the more she felt it sounded like a possible career for her. She contacted the speech and language therapy department in her local hospital and they invited her to visit so that she could talk to some of their therapists. They were not able to offer her the opportunity to watch them working with patients as the therapists were already working with several students from the local university and did not have the facilities. However, they suggested she should attend a careers evening arranged by the local health authority as well as the open day that they would be holding at the hospital later in the year.

Kirsty's expectations were confirmed. Not only did the work sound interesting, but it also looked fascinating on the videos they were shown.

Because she had a good first degree, Kirsty was advised by one of the universities running a speech and language therapy course that she was eligible to apply for their Master's degree programme so that she could become a speech and language therapist in two years. They warned her that it was full-time and that the number of weeks per term would be more than those on the undergraduate degree. They also told her that the work would be very intensive. But by that time Kirsty was convinced that this was the career for her.

She had already heard that it was difficult to get accepted onto such a course because the competition was so great. In order to increase her chances of acceptance she decided not to apply until the following year. This would then give her time to gain additional experience before applying.

She continued to work as a volunteer, this time in a residential home for elderly people, and was then fortunate enough to be offered a paid job as a speech and language therapy assistant in a paediatric speech and language therapy team. She worked mainly in a special school alongside one therapist. But because the speech and language therapy manager knew about her ambitions Kirsty was given the opportunity to observe the other therapists in the team who worked in mainstream schools and other special schools in the area.

As she gained more experience, the therapist with whom she worked in the special school felt confident enough to leave Kirsty to continue the therapy with the children whenever she had to attend meetings, and Kirsty found that her own confidence began to grow. In order to broaden her experience with different groups of people with impaired communication,

Kirsty became a volunteer with the Stroke Association and one evening a week did a home visit to work with a man whose speech and language had been affected by a stroke.

She filled most of her leisure time with her voluntary work, as at weekends she worked with Riding for the Disabled. This for her felt more like fun than work as she was able to enjoy her own hobby of horse riding at the same time as she was learning how to communicate with young physically and cognitively disabled children.

A year later her application to the MSc course was successful, and naturally she was pleased to be accepted. Looking back now she realises that the two years she spent studying for the degree were even harder work than she had imagined. There was so much to cover, in lectures and tutorials as well as her own reading, and she also had to prepare for her practical work. On placement, integrating the theory she was learning in university was a very demanding task. There was regular course work to be handed in and she also found it hard work having to revise for the final examinations, particularly when the weather was good.

There were times when she did wonder if she would be able to make it through to the end of the course, but then she realised that everyone else was feeling the same way. Fortunately, within her year group there was a strong sense of group support with everyone encouraging each other. Kirsty had always felt very committed to the work and she is glad that she persevered as she loves her job now that she has qualified. The variety of her work is almost as great as when she was working with several different voluntary organisations and her greatest reward is that she has a clear sense that she is making a difference to people's lives.

She has now been qualified for two years and is working in what is called a 'split post' so that she sees children on Mondays, Tuesdays and Wednesdays and works with adults on

Thursdays and Fridays. She did not have any difficulty getting a job once she qualified; in fact she had three successful interviews in different places so that her only problem was deciding which job to take. Her previous life- and work-experience proved helpful in making the decision.

One of the things she likes most about the job she chose is that she received regular supervision when she most needed it – as a newly qualified therapist. Even now she is always well supported not only by her line-manager but also by her immediate superiors and by all her colleagues.

Some of her year group from the university have already begun to specialise but Kirsty still enjoys being able to work with adults and with children. She never ceases to be amazed at the number of different types of problems she deals with every week.

This week she saw Rosie who had had her cleft lip and palate repaired at a specialist teaching hospital. Rosie's speech is now quite clear but Kirsty will continue to work with her regularly in clinic to help her language development as it is delayed.

When Rosie was first referred, Kirsty found herself looking up her lecture notes to remind herself of some of the technical terms the consultant surgeon used in his detailed report about Rosie's surgery. As she had not seen any children with cleft lip and palate before she had forgotten some of the specific theoretical details. As she checked her notes she was surprised to find how quickly some of the techniques had advanced and how many new developments there had been in that area since she had qualified. But, as a member of RCSLT, Kirsty had access to the appropriate information and was able to read the relevant journals to find out more about the techniques the surgeon had described.

On Thursdays and Fridays when she works with adults, Kirsty is involved in rehabilitation work mostly with patients who are recovering from a stroke. It is on these days that she remembers the work she did before joining the course, when she was volunteering for the Stroke Association. She finds invaluable those early experiences of learning how to relate to such clients adult-to-adult, and not just as therapist-to-client. Also, she has been asked to organise the volunteers who now work in the centre and she finds she is able to understand their needs and create a mutually beneficial working atmosphere.

Kirsty has been thinking about going abroad again, perhaps in another year, and has already discussed it with her manager. Given the experience she has gained since qualifying she knows she would have much to offer a VSO team. Through the RCSLT she has been in touch with other therapists who have worked overseas and she hopes to make her decision soon.

Chapter 18 Working with people with learning disabilities

Sam is working with people with learning disabilities although this is not a client group she ever imagined she would work with. When she was on the speech and language therapy course at university four years ago there were lectures about people with learning disabilities, but Sam had never had the opportunity to work with either children or adults who had such problems on any of her placements. Consequently, when her speech and language therapy manager in her first job asked her if she would like to spend some of the week working in this area she did not feel confident about accepting.

However, she then remembered that her clinical tutor at the university had always told her that many of the skills she would develop as a student were 'transferable skills' and if faced with a different client group she would need to identify what skills she had already developed with other clients that would be applicable to working with the new group. When Sam approached her manager's suggestion in that way she found she had more than adequate clinical and professional skills – and knowledge – to rise to the new challenge.

At first she joined the learning disabilities team for only two days a week. However, Sam found the team leader inspirational and enjoyed the multi-disciplinary teamwork as she found herself working with professionals such as nurses, social workers and occupational therapists. She was surprised at how quickly her own enthusiasm for the work was growing. She now is totally committed to working with this new client group and works with the team full-time.

She recognises that, because of the nature of their difficulties, progress for such clients is often extremely slow, but she has learned to set small, realistic and achievable targets that are directly relevant to the clients' everyday lives and she can see how in so many cases she has been able to help them improve the quality of their lives, even if only in some small way.

One of the projects Sam has been involved with during the last year has been preparing four adults who had lived in a large residential home to move to a new house which has been provided just for the four of them. The three men and one woman are all in their late forties and early fifties and no longer have any close family ties. For them this move will mean a huge change and upheaval in their lives. During the day they all attend a day centre and Sam has had to liaise with the staff at that centre as well as with the residential staff at the house.

Living in the large residential home for most of their lives has meant that the clients are used to having everything provided for them and as a result have become very passive. It is quite a challenge for Sam and the support workers to set up opportunities so that the clients can now begin to make some choices for themselves. The team need to show them how they can have some influence over their own lives even if only in small ways.

Sam has been working with the occupational therapist trying to encourage the clients to be more active, to initiate and take part in activities. She has made a referral to the community support workers in her local learning disabilities team so that they can work with the clients, training them regarding travel and shopping. Sam has also had meetings with the community support workers looking at how they might encourage the clients' communications skills in these activities.

Sam has been observing the clients in the residential home and at the day centre to assess their communication skills. She uses detailed assessment checklists when looking at the clients' interactional skills, their personal and social skills, as well as when assessing their comprehension and expressive language, and their non-verbal communication. As there are few published standardised assessments that can by used with this client group, Sam creates her own assessment materials based on her knowledge and experience. She also looks at the communication used by the support staff when interacting with the clients.

Sam visits the centre and the home together with the community support workers. She gathers together all the information to write reports on the communication skills of the clients and she is then able to make recommendations about how these skills may be developed. The support staff are more familiar with the clients than she is so Sam makes sure that they understand and agree with the information in the reports, and that the clients understand the recommendations that have been made. This is achieved by the use of photographs and symbols where necessary as well as ensuring the information is written in plain language without jargon.

As there is money available for some dramatherapy sessions, Sam has had the opportunity to work with a dramatherapist. Together they have devised some scenarios that will help prepare the clients for their move. They have found some useful information about story telling on the Internet and Sam has also made contact with other speech and language therapists who have more experience of this type of work. Sam has had to liaise with the manager of the residential home in order for support staff to be released to help work with the group.

The local learning disability service, which is an integrated service offered by health and social services, need to ensure that the move is well planned and executed. They have appointed a working group to oversee the project. This group has set targets in relation to the clients and the final move. Once a week Sam meets with her manager and a speech and language therapy colleague who is also involved in the project to check that they are on target for meeting the deadlines set by the working group. Their main aim is to help the clients cope with all the changes that are suddenly occurring in their lives, and to enable them to express their feelings about them. The therapists are trying to help the four to adjust to their new setting and to develop their social communication skills in their new environment.

When Sam asked to be transferred to work full-time with the learning disabilities team her manager offered her the opportunity for some additional training as part of her continuing professional development. Although there was a limited training budget she was told she could choose up to three short courses that she felt would help her most in her new role. Sam has, therefore, recently attended a course on Makaton signing, a course on alternative and augmentative communication systems (AAC), and a longer course learning about teaching strategies so that she is able to support and train other staff who work with clients with learning disabilities. Sam felt that, although the foundations of these skills had been laid down while she was at university, she needed to develop them further so that she could use them in specific ways to help her in her new role.

One of the most striking differences in working with the learning disabilities team from her previous clinical work is that Sam is now more involved in the role of staff training. For example, the clients who are moving are all users of Makaton signs and symbols. Sam is working with the speech and language therapist who is the Makaton trainer to train the clients' new support staff. Sam will then be able to offer ongoing support to the staff to help them use their newly learnt skills. Sam often works indirectly with the clients through the support staff, although recently she has been running a social skills group herself with an assistant speech and language therapist and a support worker.

Sam now cannot imagine working with any other client group and she is encouraged not only by her own commitment to the work and to the clients, but also by the commitment of all those who are working with them. This, of course, contributes to making the work even more enjoyable.

Her manager has suggested that she might like to spend some time with one of the other speech and language therapy teams in the area who collaborate with other therapists and psychologists working with people who have mental health problems. These include people who have schizophrenia, clinical depression, or who suffer from substance abuse, self-injurious behaviour or eating disorders. She has already come across some mental health issues among a few of her current clients although she knows the two groups are quite different.

In the meantime, she has asked to attend two more short courses next year. One is on 'intensive interaction' as this will help her work with clients with more complex needs and another is a course on 'story narrative'. She feels both of these courses will help her develop some new ways of thinking and working in her current setting.

Chapter 19 A speech and language therapy manager

Charlotte has been a speech and language therapist for over sixteen years. She is the senior speech and language therapist in a busy ENT (ear, nose and throat) department in a city hospital. She manages the speech and language therapy service in her own hospital where she is responsible for three full-time therapists and two part-time therapists in her team.

Charlotte has three days a week allocated to her clinical work that includes the time needed for administration relevant to that work. She sees her patients on the ward and as out-patients. Once a month she jointly runs a specialist head-and-neck clinic and she also runs a dysphagia clinic.

Charlotte became interested in this type of clinical work as a result of her first speech and language therapy job where she spent a day a week in an ENT department. The work is varied and currently includes Val, a teacher whose voice has become hoarse and inaudible for the third time in a year; Toby a young boy who keeps losing his voice because of too much shouting and screaming, and Tom, a factory worker who has just had a laryngectomy. Tom had cancer of the throat and his larynx (voice box) was removed leaving him with a stoma (a permanent opening in his neck) and no immediate way to speak or communicate.

Charlotte started by finding a way for Tom to communicate, without speech, while in hospital and is now helping him learn a new method of communication. Part of her role is teaching Tom how to take care of his stoma. Also, because his since his operation, Charlotte has had to help him deal with the emotional trauma of suddenly losing his natural means of communication. Before she can help Tom to use an alternative method of communication she has to help him adjust to his new situation.

Working with patients with voice problems can be even more emotionally demanding than working in many other aspects of speech and language therapy because voice problems are often associated with emotional difficulties. For example, Charlotte recently worked with Jane who has now been discharged. Jane was originally referred because she was diagnosed with aphonia – total loss of her voice. Investigations showed that there were no physical reasons for Jane's voice loss and that the cause of the problem was psychological, as Jane had recently suffered a major and ongoing trauma that she had had great difficulty coping with.

Charlotte improved her listening skills and learned how to support patients during her training. However, with both of these patients Charlotte has found it very helpful that she has previously studied for a counselling diploma. She does not work as a counsellor but finds the skills and knowledge she learned on the course invaluable when working with such patients. She is able to listen with greater understanding and knows when she needs to refer patients on to a professional counsellor or to a psychotherapist.

Charlotte enjoys the variety of her clinical work which means she spends time on the wards, in specialist multi-disciplinary clinics and seeing patients on a one-to-one or group basis in her own out-patient clinics. She also sees patients coming in for day surgery to advise about vocal care in the immediate post-operative period and to set up their first speech and language therapy appointment following voice rest.

She enjoys working as part of a team in her clinical work as she works with many different professionals including ENT consultants, head and neck surgeons, radiologists, members of the nursing team and dieticians, as well as voice teachers and trainers.

Charlotte is happy to be involved in student training and enjoys working with speech and language therapy students and junior members of staff who want to develop their clinical skills in this area.

She is a member of the Voice Association where she is able to share her knowledge with other professionals and she also belongs to the RCSLT Special Interest Group (SIG) for voice, which keeps her up-to-date.

Two days a week are allocated to Charlotte's management activities. Her management duties relating directly to the therapists in her team include collecting relevant statistics, and developing workable systems to ensure that the best service is offered to the patients. She also has to ensure that her therapists work together as a team and she enables them to work collaboratively with other members of the multi-disciplinary team such as physiotherapists, specialist nurses and occupational therapists.

Charlotte is responsible for all aspects of the welfare of the speech and language therapy team. Part of her role is to look at recruitment and retention of her staff. Charlotte is involved in interviewing new team members and has responsibility to manage issues relating to staff absence and occupational health issues. She also ensures that their caseloads and workloads are realistic and that they are managing their work within the time available.

She is responsible for developing systems for support and supervision within the team and is also responsible for organising the monitoring and evaluation of their work. One way she does this is through individual performance reviews that allow staff members to think about their future career development and to identify training and development needs.

When thinking about the organisation of the speech and language therapy department Charlotte is responsible for future workforce planning so she has to be aware when staff contracts terminate. She also has to think about recruitment drives and to put in bids for her budget requirements. She has to bid for equipment and resources and often has to write detailed reports to support her case. If the money is not forthcoming, she may have to think of innovative ways of adding resources to her department.

Charlotte has to attend managerial meetings that are less directly related to specific speech and language therapy issues, although they have an impact on how she and her team work. She is involved in writing policy documents, liaising with departmental heads, and meeting with staff who are involved in monitoring and evaluating new procedures and strategy development within the hospital generally. For example, she is working with a small group of managers from other departments, monitoring the types of referrals received so that they can make sure the hospital is offering the most appropriate type of provision.

One of the most difficult aspects for Charlotte is to find time in her diary for any emergency management issues that might arise, such as when she has to respond quickly to a request from her own line-manager who is a senior nurse. For example, recently there was a patient-related complaint requiring an immediate response and Charlotte was asked to provide some data urgently. She didn't have access to the information directly herself and relied on the other members of her team to respond quickly. Gathering the information and presenting it to her own manager in an appropriate form proved to be very time consuming and in order to meet the tight deadline Charlotte had to reorganise her workload priorities that week.

The management side of her work has gradually grown while she has been in this job and because of the constant changes that have taken place in recent years within the NHS she always has to be ready for a new challenge.

However, Charlotte really enjoys the managerial aspects of her work and would ultimately like to take a sideways step towards promotion by becoming a service manager in the NHS, rather than advancing in speech and language therapy. She will need to take a wider view then of the needs of the service as a whole. She knows that she needs to develop transferable skills and flexibility so, in order to prepare for this, she is accepting small pieces of work as they become available within the hospital that are not related to speech and language therapy directly. This is the result of a recent decision to second her to work as part of the Trust's management team one day a week. She is pleased with this arrangement. She is now beginning to encourage her team members to start to develop their management skills too.

Such work will help her to develop new skills that she can add to her CV. For example, recently she has been overseeing the work of the whole of the rehabilitation team. She has also been asked to write service level agreements for the whole Trust. In the future she plans to do an MBA (Master's degree in Business Administration) or a Master's in Health Service Management. She knows it will be very demanding but she is pleased to have the opportunity to develop her career in such an innovative way.

Chapter 20 Working in a school for deaf children

Angela returned to work six months ago when her youngest child started nursery. She was delighted that she was able to return to the school for deaf children where she had worked previously and she found that there had been some changes since she took a career break. There are not many schools like this in the UK as it is a BSL school. Angela was aware that there are limited opportunities for therapists working in such specialised settings.

When she first worked at the school she was employed by the local health authority but that is no longer the case as the school now employs its own speech and language therapists. This is a great advantage to Angela as she is fully integrated in the staff team, and it means she only works in term time, having the same holiday breaks as her own children who are at school in the same local education authority.

Angela has always been interested in working with deaf children as her younger brother is deaf and she grew up learning BSL as he did. She joined him at the deaf club he belonged to so that she could practise using it in a social setting and although it is not her first language she did become a fluent BSL signer.

While she was at university doing her speech and language therapy degree course, Angela worked with many different client groups, but she always planned to work with deaf people. Shortly after qualifying she completed the Advanced Clinical Studies course in hearing impairment. By studying for an additional year she was able to complete a Master's degree at the same time but this was quite stressful. However, she has always enjoyed this specialised work and does not want to do any other kind of work.

The school that Angela now works in is a special school

for children from three to eleven years, all of whom have a severe to profound hearing loss. The children at this school come from a wide geographic area and are funded to attend by their own local authority.

The school has a policy of 'sign bilingualism'. For most of the children their first language is BSL, the language of the deaf community. English, the language of the hearing community, is taught as an additional language so that most children become competent in both. It is the policy of this school to use BSL in all public places within the school.

When she first returned to work after her career break Angela found that her signing was not as fluent as it had been, but it has rapidly improved since then so that she has no difficulties in being included in all conversations in the staff room.

Because of the severe nature of their hearing loss most of the children have binaural hearing aids – one in each ear. These usually have a radio aid, a special attachment clipped to the bottom of the aid that enables each child to hear the teacher directly when in the classroom or even in the playground. Many of the children now have digital aids with pre-set personalised settings.

In class, BSL is the language used for teaching but Angela also works on a daily basis with the teachers, modelling spoken and written English. This helps the children to develop their speaking and listening skills in English so that they can communicate with hearing people and can learn to switch between BSL and English.

Angela works closely with the teachers of the deaf and the LSAs in the school. In each classroom there is a teacher and an LSA, one of whom is deaf, one of whom is hearing. This usually means that one of them will be a native BSL user while the other will be fluent in BSL. Angela communicates with both of them in BSL. However, many of the staff are expert at lip reading and some of them can use spoken English themselves.

In staff meetings all the business is conducted in BSL. Most of the teaching staff have already completed their specialist teacher training which qualifies them to work with deaf children, although some are completing their studies while they are working. Angela has a good relationship with all the staff as well as with the educational psychologist and the audiologist who manages the hearing aids.

Angela takes part in the regular meetings that are held with the parents. She uses BSL when communicating with the parents who are deaf, although some of the parents who are not deaf are not fluent signers. The school holds weekly classes for parents who want to learn BSL. It also runs a drop-in group for babies and toddlers so that parents and children, who may one day attend the school, can learn BSL in a natural environment.

Angela and the other speech and language therapists in the school work closely alongside the teachers contributing to the planning and helping to run sessions with the teachers or LSAs in the classroom. For example, they work together on the development of the children's social skills and work on the children's appropriate use of language in social situations whether it is in spoken language or BSL. The teacher or the LSA will then continue that work on the days when Angela is working in another class. Most of Angela's language development and speech work is carried out in the classroom, but if children need specific help she withdraws them from the class to work with them individually.

Another aspect of Angela's work is to run in-service training sessions with the teaching staff when she will look at the role of the therapists when working with the teachers.

Previously Angela offered a placement to a third year undergraduate student who came to work with her one day a week, and on her return she informed the local university that she was back at work. It is a requirement of the school that any student working there needs to have at least Stage 1 level of BSL and Angela is hoping that the university will find someone appropriate to send to the school as she has always enjoyed working with students.

Part III
Applying for a Speech and
Language Therapy Course

Chapter 21 How to set about becoming a speech and language therapist

Having decided this might be the career for you, you now need to think about finding out more about speech and language therapy first hand and then about applying for a course.

As speech and language therapy is an all-graduate profession, in order to practise you need a qualification from one of the recognised, accredited speech and language therapy courses run within one of the higher education institutions in the UK.

Routes into the profession

There are currently two routes available to become a therapist. There is the undergraduate route resulting in a Bachelor's degree, which in some universities is an honours degree; or a post-graduate route, which results either in a post-graduate diploma or Master's degree depending on the university.

Most universities offer a Bachelor/Master of Science although the degrees have a variety of different titles. These include:

- BSc /BScHons Speech Pathology and Therapy
- BSc /BSc Hons Human Communication
- BSc in Linguistics and Language Pathology
- BSc Hons Clinical Language Sciences
- BSc Hons Speech and Language Therapy
- BSc Hons Speech and Language Sciences
- BMedSci Hons Speech
- BSc Speech Sciences
- BSc Hons Speech Pathology and Therapy
- BSc Hons Psychology and Speech Pathology
- BSc/BSc Hons Speech and Language Pathology

- BSc Hons Human Communication Studies

- MSc Language Pathology
- MMedSci Clinical Communication Studies
- MSc/PGDip Speech and Language Therapy
- MSc Speech and Language Science

Despite the different names, all of the degrees from the universities with accredited speech and language therapy courses enable you to apply for registration as a speech and language therapist to the Health Professionals Council (HPC) and to be recommended for membership of the RCSLT.

The nature of the courses

All the courses cover the general topics outlined in Part IV and will generally include psychology, linguistics, speech and language pathology, neurology, anatomy and physiology and medical aspects, and social and educational aspects. They will all also include at least the minimum required number of hours for students to work on placement under the supervision of a qualified speech and language therapist. However, each course will have a different emphasis. So, for example, one may be more medically orientated, whereas another may be more linguistically focussed. Some courses may require a final research dissertation; others may include a detailed case study but no dissertation.

　　The courses differ in length and the ways in which they are planned may differ as well. For example, some courses will be offered as part of a modular system requiring you to achieve a 'pass' at one level before you move on the next. Others may be divided into units and you will be required to 'pass' a specific number of units overall in order to obtain the degree. Some universities divide the year into two longer terms (a semester system), others have three terms with long summer holidays like the school trimester system. The length of holidays will differ too as you may be required to work for extended periods on placement.

On most of the Master's courses you will find that you are required to work a full calendar year rather than an academic year, and there will be only minimum holidays with a much reduced summer break.

Intensity and hard work

Whichever route you choose, you will be involved in a considerable amount of hard work. Most speech and language therapy courses involve more contact hours than many other degrees so you need to be prepared to spend more time in college than many other students. You will often find you are obliged to attend more timetabled lectures, seminars and tutorials than many other students and that some of these will be compulsory. This is because the course includes a professional training and in addition to college-based studies you will be involved in a large element of practical work.

Usually you attend a placement either on a day-release basis or as a 'block' over a period of weeks, sometimes months. You will find that you will need to spend a considerable amount of time preparing for and evaluating your practical work. This often means there is not as much time available for you to enjoy a full student social life like students on other courses. As with other courses that offer a degree and a professional qualification, they are by definition more demanding of students on a variety of levels and the 'student experience' may also be more emotionally demanding than other courses. However, speech and language therapy students usually agree that the end result and the enjoyment of the work reap their own rewards.

The end result

Once you have successfully completed your course you will not only have a Bachelor's or Master's degree (or possibly a post-graduate diploma) you will also have a professional qualification. You will be recommended for membership of the RCSLT and you will be eligible to apply to the HPC for registration as a speech and language therapist. This allows you to practise as a therapist anywhere in the UK. It may also be possible to practise in some other countries and this is discussed further in Part V.

Chapter 22 Where can you train?

There are currently sixteen courses at universities throughout the UK where you can study at undergraduate level to become a speech and language therapist. This includes two in Scotland, one in Wales and one in Northern Ireland. Five of the English courses offer Master's degree programmes as well. There are also four in the Republic of Ireland three at undergraduate and one at post-graduate level.

Figure 15 University courses in the UK

Queen Margaret University College Department of Speech and Language Sciences Clerwood Terrace Edinburgh EH12 8TS	BSc (Hons)
De Montfort University Department of Human Communication De Montfort University Scraptoft Campus Scraptoft Leicester LE7 9SU	BSc /BSc (Hons)
University of Wales Institute Cardiff Centre for Speech and Language Therapy Studies Faculty of Community Health Sciences Western Avenue Llandaff, Cardiff CF5 2YB	BSc/BSc (Hons)

University of Manchester Centre for Human Communication and Deafness School of Education Oxford Road Manchester M13 9PL	BSc (Hons)
Manchester Metropolitan University Department of Psychology and Speech Pathology Hathersage Road Manchester M13 0JA	BSc (Hons)
University of Ulster at Jordanstown School of Behavioural and Communication Sciences Faculty of Social and Health Sciences and Education Shore Road Newtownabbey Co.Antrim BT37 0QB	BSc (Hons)
Leeds Metropolitan University School of Applied Social Sciences Group Calverly Street Leeds LS1 3HE	BSc (Hons)
City University Department of Language and Communication Science Northampton Square London EC1V OHB	BSc (Hons) PgDip/MSc

University of Central England in Birmingham School of Health and Policy Studies Franchise Street Perry Barr Birmingham B42 2SU	BSc (Hons)
University of Strathclyde Faculty of Education Jordanhill Campus Department of Speech and Language Therapy 76 Southbrae Drive Glasgow G13 1PP	BSc /BSc (Hons)
College of St Mark and St John Department of Speech and Hearing Sciences Derriford Road Plymouth PL6 8BH	BSc (Hons)
University of East Anglia School of Allied Health Professions University of East Anglia Norwich NR4 7TJ	BSc (Hons)
Universtity College London Department of Human Communication Science Chandler House 2 Wakefield Street London WC1N 1PF	BSc (Hons) MSc

University of Reading Communication Disorders Centre School of Linguistics and Applied Language Whiteknights Reading Berkshire RG6 6AA	BSc MSc
University of Sheffield Department of Human Communication Sciences 12/20/31 Claremont Crescent Sheffield S10 2TA	BmedSci (Hons) MMedSci
University of Newcastle upon Tyne Speech and Langue Sciences Section School of Education, Communication and Language Sciences King George VI Building Queen Victoria Road Newcastle upon Tyne NE1 7RU	BSc (Hons) MSc

Additional courses in the Republic of Ireland are at:

Trinity College Dublin - BSc
National University of Ireland – Cork - BSc
National University of Ireland, Galway - BSc
University of Limerick - MSc

Chapter 23 Entry requirements

The undergraduate route will take three or four years depending on where you study. For this you will need 'A' levels or Scottish or Irish Highers, or an Access course, or a mature student profile as discussed below.

The post-graduate route may take two or three years depending on where you study and for these courses you will need a first degree.

Undergraduate degrees

Students applying straight from school

The requirements will differ slightly between universities and you should look carefully at the individual requirements of the universities of your choice. If you have settled on your career choice before you embark on your 'A' level programme, you would be able to consider some of these requirements before deciding on your choice of subjects.

There is an expectation that all candidates applying for speech and language therapy courses will satisfy the basic university general entrance requirements and you apply for speech and language therapy courses, as you would for any course, through the UCAS system.

If you are studying for 'A' levels, the grades you will be asked for will differ depending on the university but you will probably be asked for grades varying from ABB to BBC with an additional pass at AS level. Some universities will specify that you must have a science at 'A' level such as biology; others will not be so specific. You must make sure you comply with the individual requirements of the universities to which you are applying.

Even where subjects are not specified there are some subjects such as biology, or maths, that will be helpful to you and it will be important to ensure you have a pass at least at GCSE level.

Candidates taking Scottish or Irish Highers or the International Baccalaureate will need to look at the individual requirements of the universities.

Mature applicants

If you are a mature applicant you will also be applying through UCAS although, here, details about the life experience you've gained since leaving school will be an important focus of your application. If you don't have a degree you will normally be asked to provide evidence of recent study, such as taking a subject at AS level or studying on an Access course. This will help to show that you are able to apply yourself to the kind of intensive study required for the course.

Mature applicants who have a degree may want to consider following the post-graduate route discussed below. However, most universities have a limited number of places on their Master's programmes compared with their undergraduate programmes and competition is therefore extremely fierce. On some courses only about 10% or less of those applying are successful. If you didn't get a high classification in your first degree this will significantly reduce your chances of being successful in a post-graduate application. Some mature students, therefore, even if they have a first degree, take the decision to apply for an undergraduate course. Many students find that having a longer period in which to study better suits their personal circumstances and it also provides additional time for the development of clinical and professional skills.

Post-graduate degrees

Overall, there are far fewer places available on the post-graduate programmes in the UK than on undergraduate programmes and, as mentioned above, there is much competition for these places. Most universities will be looking for a first degree classification of 2:1 or above and some – although not all – may specify that the subject of the degree is speech and language therapy 'related', such as linguistics or psychology.

In order to increase your chances for selection, it will be important for you to demonstrate not only your excellent academic skills but also your commitment to your newly chosen career. And, of course, you will need both of these elements if you are to complete the course successfully.

Before taking the decision to undertake a period of such intensive study, it makes sense for you to find out as much as you can about speech and language therapy as a career. You will then be able to use this knowledge and experience to demonstrate your commitment.

For example, it will be helpful if you can provide evidence that you have taken the initiative in finding out as much about the profession as possible through visits, talking to relevant people, reading books or articles, and from the Internet. You should try to gain some practical experience by working with people with communication disorders, either through some form of paid work or as a volunteer.

Chapter 24 Funding

At the time of writing, the undergraduate and post-graduate fees for all home and EU speech and language therapy students studying in the UK are paid by the NHS and you will not be required to pay any additional top-up fee. However, as you will be aware there are proposed changes to student fees and grants and it will be important for you to check for the latest information for the year for which you are applying on the NHS Student Grants Unit website given in *Useful Addresses*.

Home students' bursary

Currently, students are eligible to apply for a means-tested bursary that will also be awarded by the NHS. Normally, in order to be eligible for such a bursary, you need to have been resident in the UK for three years prior to the start of the course. The amount of the award will depend on the income of your spouse, or if you are under the age of 25, on the income of your parents, or possibly your own income if you are able to earn during your period of study. This means that any relevant income will be taken into account and the amount of the bursary will be reduced proportionately. If you are claiming an NHS means-tested bursary you may also be entitled to apply for a student loan.

Although the legislation regarding fees and bursaries does apply generally to students from the UK there are some additional adjustments that may apply to applicants from Scotland and Northern Ireland. It is, therefore, recommended that you check for the latest details of funding with the Students Award Agency for Scotland and The Department for Higher and Further Education Northern Ireland (see *Useful Addresses*).

EU students

Currently fees are paid for all applicants from the EU, but these students are not eligible for a bursary.

International Students

Universities welcome enquiries from international students who are interested in a speech and language therapy qualification. However, although the qualification enables you to work as a therapist in the UK it does not in any way guarantee or qualify you for a work permit. Equally, unless there is reciprocal recognition with your country of origin it will not necessarily qualify you to work as a speech and language therapist when you return home.

Students applying from outside the UK and EU are not eligible for any NHS funding and will normally be expected to pay the university's full overseas student rates themselves.

International students will be considered for entry onto a degree programme in the UK provided that their qualifications satisfy the entry requirements of the individual university. In addition, all students whose first language is not English are required to provide recent evidence of their ability to understand and use English to a standard that will ensure that language problems in English will not impede their academic progress. The current recommendation from RCSLT that is used by most universities is that applicants should have achieved a minimum grade of 7.5 with a grade of no lower than 7.0 in any one of the four sub tests of the British Council International English Language Testing System (IELTS). Some universities may require a higher grade and it will be important to check with an individual university before applying. The application and interview process will vary according to the university.

Chapter 25 Making initial contact

You probably won't need to make personal contact with an individual university as all the information you need will usually be available from the universities' prospectuses, websites or the UCAS website. If, for any reason, you do feel you need to make telephone contact then you will need to remember that even by making a casual enquiry you will also be making the all important first impression on the admissions tutor, or the administrative staff.

It's also worth remembering that, whoever you speak to, admissions is probably only one part of their job. They probably have to deal with hundreds of similar queries to yours, at the same time as being busy with other work; so don't waste time. Be concise, have your questions ready and thought-through and, although it may sound obvious, make sure you know the full name of the course you are interested in. Many departments have several similar sounding courses and it is easy to confuse them.

Be assertive, asking your questions clearly and politely. But don't be rude, sound agitated, or get impatient or angry. If you are aggressive in any way you might be remembered for all the wrong reasons!

Chapter 26 Skills, qualities and experience

You should begin to gather information – and experience – from the moment you feel you are interested in speech and language therapy as a career and you should continue gathering this information and experience even after you are offered a place.

Initially, your experiences will help you decide whether this is indeed the career for you. Then they should be able to help you to present yourself on paper as a well-informed applicant and increase your chances of being interviewed by the departments that call candidates for interview. These experiences will be the evidence of your commitment and interest.

If you are offered a place at one of the universities then it will be important to continue to work with people with communication disorders until you start the course so that you have as much experience as possible. It would be helpful if you could to learn how to relate to people of widely differing age groups – young children who are acquiring their speech and language, or elderly people whose language is beginning to break down. This will all be useful to you once you have begun the course.

How to gain relevant experience

Within school

There are many roles you could take within school that would help you to understand what it is like to be able to support others, to work with others, to be a team member and to take on responsibility. It would be helpful if you could take on such challenges for example by being a mentor, helping others with their reading, taking on a role of responsibility such as captaining a sports team, chairing a society, or being a prefect.

School work-experience

If you are offered the opportunity to undertake some work experience while you are still at school you could use it to help you decide whether speech and language therapy is the career for you. It may be possible for you to do some work at your local speech and language therapy department. If this is not possible then you may be able to work in schools or in nurseries. You may find some work in a hospital setting, or in a home for elderly people, at a club for deaf people, or a day centre or hostel for people with severe learning disabilities.

As a mature student

Observe and read

You should take all opportunities to gain as much experience and knowledge as you can about people with communication problems. While ideally you would want to observe a speech and language therapist at work this may not always be possible. Some speech and language therapy departments however offer talks or demonstrations, or you may be able to attend a one or two day course (check the RCSLT website for details). Ask at your local library for videos of people with communication problems and read a range of books. Some initial books and video titles are suggested in the *Further Reading* section of this book.

Paid or voluntary work

It may be possible to work directly with speech and language therapists as a speech and language therapy assistant, or you may be accepted for voluntary work in schools or nurseries, homes for elderly people, hospitals, or day centres, or for a relevant charity.

Opportunities to communicate

If paid or unpaid work is not an option, then try and find a way of making sure you talk to a speech and language therapist so that you can find out first-hand about the job. Spend as much time as possible talking to different people who have communication problems. Visit a local stroke club; attend a social club for people with learning disabilities; volunteer for hospital visiting, or read books to blind people.

You might find it helpful to learn how to communicate through a different medium by joining a community club for deaf people. Many applicants who are interested in different aspects of communication begin to learn BSL. This helps provide an insight into different patterns of communication and will often prove to be a useful skill within specific, specialised clinical placements while on the course.

Speech and language therapy is about working with people, not only on a one-to-one basis but also in large and small groups. Make sure this is something you really enjoy doing.

Chapter 27 Filling out the application form

So, now you have decided this is the career for you, you can begin to fill out the application form.

If you have not previously made contact with the university department, this will be your first opportunity to make a positive impression on the admissions tutor who will be reading your form and who will be involved in the whole selection process including, where relevant, the interview.

The admissions tutor will be looking for evidence:
-   that you have made an informed career choice based on serious thought and discussion;
-   that you are aware of the type of subjects you will be required to study;
-   that you are aware of the intensity of the study and the practical aspects of the work.

Presentation

It's important when completing your application form –
  ➢ to make sure it's legible;
  ➢ to ensure there is no crossing out if it's handwritten;
  ➢ to ensure there are no typing errors if you have processed it;
  ➢ to check it again for the kind of spelling mistakes even a spell-check can miss;
  ➢ to make sure you haven't left out any important details about you;
  ➢ to get someone else to read it as it is easy to make a mistake.

It is always a good idea to photocopy the form so that you can refresh your memory if you have to attend for interview.

References

Most universities prefer an academic reference and even if you completed your first degree some time ago you should still be able to obtain a copy of your final academic reference from the institution where you undertook your original studies.

Any other referee you name should be able to write about your ability to apply yourself to an intensive academic course as well your ability to work ultimately as a speech and language therapist.

If you are asked to supply an additional referee and you have worked as an assistant it would be important for your line-manager, the person to whom you were directly responsible, to be one of your referees.

Personal statement

Whichever course you apply for, you will have to complete some form of personal statement, whether you are filling in a UCAS form for an undergraduate place or applying directly to the university for a post-graduate place.

Undergraduate

When filling out a UCAS form, the personal statement should include:
- ❖ reference to any observations you have made of a speech and language therapist at work;
- ❖ any specifically relevant work experience you may have had;
- ❖ a summary about how you think any other kind of work experience, or your particular interests or hobbies, might relate to you becoming a therapist.

Post-graduate

Post-graduate applicants will normally complete a form sent directly from the university and many universities prefer you to complete the form rather than sending in a separately typed CV. On the personal statement you will need to refer to:
- ❖ why you made this career choice;
- ❖ relevant work experience;
- ❖ observations of therapists at work;
- ❖ discussions with therapists;
- ❖ courses attended.

In addition you will need:
- ❖ to say how you feel your previous skills and experiences, either from your previous career or your first degree, should help equip you to work as a speech and language therapist;
- ❖ to discuss why you want to do this course at this university;
- ❖ to demonstrate your commitment to completing an intensive and difficult course;
- ❖ to offer reasons for your career change.

Mentioning any difficulties and potential obstacles

If you have any form of disability, or if there is anything in your medical or mental health background that could impede your studies in any way, it is better for you to mention this either on the application form or at the time of interview. The best option, if possible, is to seek to discuss the situation with the admissions tutor. S/he will normally be able to discuss the matter with you, in confidence, and this could save endless hours of difficulties later. It may be something for which help and support can be provided, or it may be that the ultimate career choice is not for you, but it is better to find out now than to suffer disappointment part way through the course, or at the end of the course.

Police check

You should also be aware that before being sent on placement you will, as a student, be subject to a routine police investigation to ensure that there is no reason why you should not be working with children and vulnerable people.

Planning for a gap year

It has become increasingly accepted that potential undergraduate students may want to take a year out between school and university and most universities will actively encourage this. This of course does not apply to post-graduate students.

Some students prefer to wait until they come back before they apply to university. However, you can apply for entry into the following year if you know beforehand, that you intend to take a year out.

There are ways in which your gap year can be used, not only to give you new experiences and to help you broaden your horizons, but also to help you with your future studies. If you are planning to take a gap year, then admissions tutors will be looking for evidence that you are structuring your year appropriately, in a way that will help you in your chosen career. You will need to show how you hope to benefit from your experience, and demonstrate ways in which it will help you develop your confidence and your general skills. How to make the most of your gap year is discussed in more detail below.

How to make the most of a gap year

A gap year usually helps you to mature and become more confident. It offers the opportunity – possibly for the first time – for you to be independent, to travel or work away from home, away from parental and school pressures. For many of you it may be the first chance you've had to learn about looking after yourself – taking responsibility for such basic skills as ensuring you eat, washing your own clothes, managing your own finances and being responsible for your own health and general care.

It's also a wonderful opportunity to enhance your CV and to gain some additional skills by providing time for more in-depth experiences. So, if you do decide to take a gap year it will be important to plan it carefully. There are many websites and books available to help you plan and organise and give you a direction for the year, but it would be even more beneficial if you were able to include in your experiences things that will eventually help you in your work as a speech and language therapist, in a setting where you will at least not be assessed and scrutinised as you will be at university.

For example, if you are taking a trip, it will not only help you to see how others live but will also help you to experience – and hopefully develop a greater understanding and tolerance of – people from different cultures and backgrounds. If you were working abroad you would become aware of different cultural attitudes to people with communication difficulties. You may have the possibility of trying to learn a new language, experiencing first hand what it is like not being able to communicate automatically. Or, if you choose to help others to learn English, you may learn about coping with the frustration of others. It will provide you with an opportunity to try out and find out how well you can communicate in difficult circumstances.

You may choose to spend the year working in a way that is more directly related to speech and language therapy, either in the UK or abroad. This may focus on particular clients, such as volunteering in a speech and language therapy department, or a special school. Or you could work for a charity. This would give you the opportunity to become familiar with a wider variety of types of disability and to become familiar with the terminology used in different settings.

Chapter 28 Being interviewed

Preparing for interview

If a university speech and language therapy course does require you to attend for an individual interview that will be the time when you will need to 'sell yourself'. They will already know about your basic skills from your obviously impressive form-filling ability; now you have a chance to impress them with your personality.

Timing

Make sure you arrive in the best possible frame of mind. You don't want to get there feeling flustered or overanxious so check well in advance that you know how to get there, the times of the trains, the distance and route from the station. You must make sure you are on time – as this gives an immediate impression about your reliability, your time management and your organisational skills –all of which are important professional skills when working as a trainee therapist on placement.

Dress

Many people like to wear their 'best suit' and that is fine, although not a 'must'. Above all, you should feel comfortable, be confident that you look your best and ask yourself, 'Would people have confidence in me as a future therapist?'

Knowledge

It may help you feel more prepared if you have prior knowledge about the department you are visiting and information can usually be found in a prospectus or on a departmental website. Try and find out what differentiates one course from another so that if asked you would be able to explain why you have chosen that particular department.

If the course is in a department which has a strong science focus be prepared to answer questions about how you would cope with the science aspects of the course if your previous studies and qualifications are stronger on the arts side.

Questions

You will usually be asked if you have any questions, so it would be as well to think of any questions beforehand that you want answered. Write them down as you are bound to forget something in the excitement of the day, and check that all your questions have been answered before you leave the department.

Rehearsal

It can sometimes help if a friend can give you a practice run so that you can get used to answering questions. This might help you to be more aware of your responses. For example, if you know that when you're nervous you tend to talk too much you can try being more concise. Or, you might want to practice gathering your thoughts more quickly.

The interview

Some universities do not interview at all and those that do will deal with interviews in different ways. For example, in some you may have a workshop-style group experience. In others there may be some form of group interview as well as an individual interview with one, or possibly two, tutors. If there is a group interview make sure you join in the discussion.

Because of the professional nature of the course, attending for interview may feel like attending for an interview for a job, and indeed the interviewers will probably be looking at your potential for working as a professional as well as considering your academic skills.

Most interviewers will be sympathetic about your nervousness – everybody suffers in such circumstances. However, they will be looking at how you deal with that nervousness as this says much about how you will probably deal with similar situations such as working on placement.

Rule # 1 – even if you are nervous there is no need for anyone to know. Sit well back in the chair. Keep your hands as still as possible. Don't hold on to any papers unless its absolutely necessary because there is a possibility they will shake.

Rule # 2 – take the opportunity to demonstrate any knowledge you have of different client groups and different types of therapy and settings. Make sure you find an opportunity to elaborate about your observations and relevant experiences, where possible extending your personal statement.

Rule # 3 – don't be tempted to show off. Only use technical terminology if you're comfortable with it and sure of its meaning and usage. No one will expect you to have great technical knowledge.

Rule # 4 – try and think beyond any specific observations you've made. For example, show an awareness of the impact that communications problems may have on someone's life, how it might affect their family, their work (or school) and their lives generally.

Rule # 5 – do think about your presentation. It's a great time to demonstrate your interpersonal skills that are so essential for speech and language therapists.
- Make eye contact with the interviewers.
- Smile from time to time.

- Pause before answering questions to give you time to gather your thoughts.
- When you do speak use a strong, clear voice.
- Try and sound interested and interesting by using animated intonation and asking brief questions if appropriate.
- Keep a professional distance so that you don't become too familiar or inappropriately chatty – remember the interviewers are probably working to a tight time schedule and need to be fair to all interviewees.
- While you do need to extend your answers beyond 'yes' and 'no', don't offer too much excess information beyond what you are asked. Try and look for clues from your interviewers' body language about when you have used up your allotted time.

There is a photocopyable checklist to help you if you are being interviewed or attending an open day, or visiting the university. This can be found in the *Appendix* at the back of the book.

Chapter 29 Selection

You've been accepted! What should you do now?

Congratulations! No doubt you will spend some time celebrating! But when you finally come down it would be a good idea to begin preparing for the year ahead. You might want to read some books or articles, personal accounts of people with communication problems as well as initial textbooks. Try to visit more clinics to get a more rounded view of children and adults with communication problems, as well as people with swallowing difficulties. Search out more websites, for example, about types of speech and language disorders; do more voluntary work.

You've not been accepted – what next?

While you may feel you had every reason to expect to be offered a place you do have to remember there is a high demand on all speech and language therapy courses for a limited number of places. A rejection does not necessarily mean that you are not good enough, but merely that there are not enough places for the number of applicants, and more people had better qualifications than you.

You may have been placed on a waiting list, in which case you will have to decide how late you are prepared to accept an offer. Sometimes you may be offered a place at the last minute and, if you really want to accept, it would be in your interests to make yourself available up to the time term begins. You may even want to contact the department to let them know this.

Should you apply again?

If you still feel that this is the career for you, find out if it's possible to reapply. You will then need to think carefully about what you could do in the additional time to strengthen your application so that when you complete the application the following year you will be able to show how you have spent the time improving yourself appropriately.

It may be possible to get some feedback from the university, although because of the large numbers of students involved universities generally are not able to give specific details to individual applicants.

But this need not discourage you. For example, if you got as far as an interview you may assume that on paper, at least, your application was acceptable.

Either way, if you do reapply you will normally have to state that this is not your first application and you will then need to show how you have changed in the extra year available to you. You will have to provide evidence of what you have done in the additional time to support your application, how you've furthered your knowledge, or improved some of your skills. You will need to demonstrate that you've maintained your enthusiasm and motivation.

But you must also consider that if you failed at the interview it might be a good idea to reconsider your interview skills and see if you can improve them. Ask someone to do a mock interview with you. If possible, video it. Try and look at it critically and objectively.

Questions to ask yourself if you have failed at interview

- Did you really answer the questions appropriately, or did you keep straying from the point so that the interviewers had to re-ask the questions?
- Were you trying too hard to tell them what you wanted

to tell them rather than answering their specific questions?
- Were your answers too short and not detailed enough so that the interviewers had constantly to ask you more questions to encourage you to say more?
- Did you talk too much so that the interviewers were unable to get a word in?
- Were you so nervous you were unable to speak clearly?
- Was your speech clear and at the right volume or were the interviewers straining to hear and understand you?
- Were you able to make appropriate eye contact or did you look over their left shoulder or down at your knees?
- Did you look interested and engaged, or were you playing with your hair or fiddling with your nails?
- Did you smile or did you look so solemn, or without expression, that it would be difficult to imagine you working with people with communication problems?
- Were you able to show them that you had learned something about speech and language therapy from your experiences?
- Were you convincing that you would be able to empathise with people with communication problems and their families?
- Did you really demonstrate that you had the ability to study and keep up with the work on an intensive course?

Part IV
Being a Student

Chapter 30 The student group

Who is an ideal student?

There is not really a profile of an ideal student but, as discussed in Part 1, there are some skills, qualities and experiences that will help you complete the course successfully. Having been selected, the tutors obviously think you have at least some of these.

So, what can you expect once you start your course?

The student group

You will probably find yourself in a mixed group of students, all of whom have accessed the course through different routes. The size of the group will vary depending on the type of course and the university in which you are studying. On the undergraduate courses there is likely to be a mix of mature students as well as students who are coming straight from school. There will be far more women than men, although most courses are trying to encourage men to apply, and there will also be a mix of students with a variety of different ethnic, cultural and linguistic backgrounds.

   You will have your first experience of being part of a professional team when you work with the students in your year group and this will happen in different ways according to the individual university. For example, you will be put into different groups such as for shared readings, preparing seminars, or tutorial groups, or you will work with others together on placement.

   On placement you will be part of a different team as you will be working closely with your supervising therapist and other professionals such as teachers and LSAs in school settings, or physiotherapists and occupational therapists in a hospital setting.

Student membership of RCSLT

It would be an advantage if, from the start of the course, you became a student member of the professional body – RCSLT. You will only have to pay once for the whole time you are a student because your membership will last until you graduate. You will receive the RCSLT monthly *Bulletin*, written by speech and language therapists, which will help to keep you abreast of current professional issues. There is a fortnightly *Bulletin Supplement* where you will find adverts about all available jobs as well as listings about conferences, special interest groups and professional meetings you might attend.

Organising your time

Being a student at university is a different learning experience from being a pupil at school as you are responsible for organising your own work time. You will have greater autonomy, more personal independence and be expected to take responsibility for your own learning. You will also have to organise your own social time and your self-care time. If you are coming straight from school you may be doing all of these things for the first time. If you've had a gap year you may already have had some experience of looking after yourself.

If you are entering university as a mature student who has been working you will have the challenge of returning to regular study and you may feel as though your autonomy is being reduced and it will be your prioritisation skills that you will need to develop in order to juggle possible home and family commitments.

At the start of each academic year you will receive your timetable and the schedule for submitting course work and assessments. It is up to you to plan accordingly allowing time for the computer printer to break down the night before a hand-in, or for there to be a bus strike!

Most courses will include some study time in the weekly timetable. You will, however, need to develop good time-management skills so that you are able to manage successfully in the time the required reading, clinic preparation, coursework and the revision needed for assessments. Past students have suggested that it helps if you think of the course as if it were a job that will require you to be available at least from nine to five.

It may help if you plan for an hour's additional reading for each hour of lectures. You also need to allow time for travelling to placements as well as to the university – and, of course, don't forget to leave some time for fun!

Students' welfare

If you get into difficulties of any kind, such as financial, or possibly emotional, while at university, don't feel you have to struggle alone. Most courses have a personal tutoring system in order to provide some consistent support. You will probably find some kind of support is available from the student body, such as a student phone line. If you were to get into more serious difficulties you could find out about the university counselling service.

Don't forget to register with either the student health service or local doctor if you are not from the area.

How you experience the course may in some ways depend on whether you have come straight from school or whether you are a mature student.

Being a student straight from school

Accommodation

First year students are usually offered university accommodation. However, applications for a place in a hall of residence need to be made by specified deadlines and you will need to check on these for the university of your choice as places are usually allocated on a first-come-first-served basis.

One of the advantages of university accommodation is that you will be living together with other students from a range of different courses. However, student accommodation can bring its own problems. You might not find it easy to study – or sleep – with the level of noise that can occur in some halls of residence; and the social distractions may put you under great pressure.

Initially it can be hard to make new friends and keeping your door open while you are in your room could help to signal that you are willing to talk to people. A corridor of closed doors can be uninviting especially in the early days of being in a new area.

If the university does not have room in the halls of residence they should be able to help you by providing a list of privately available accommodation. Once you have started your course you may find others who are willing to share flats or houses in future years.

Homesickness

There is the possibility that at some stage, particularly during the first term and possibly the first year, students experience some homesickness. It is not always possible to predict when this might happen and students often say it occurs when they are least expecting it. This is not unusual and usually passes quickly with the support of new friends.

As a mature student

As a mature student on an undergraduate course you will be with a group of much younger students. If you haven't studied for a first degree or if it is a long time since you studied you might feel that the younger students are processing information faster, responding more quickly and appearing to be coping better than you are. This may leave you feeling deskilled, but remember that as a mature student you have many life skills to offer and you will probably find that the speed of your work will increase as the course progresses.

As a mature student on a post-graduate course you will by definition be a mature student as you will already have a first degree. Although you will have been a student before, a speech and language therapy course will probably be quite a different experience as the work on post-graduate courses is intensive with limited holidays. Entrance to such courses is competitive and you will probably find yourself in a group of students who have set themselves very high standards. There is, therefore, a risk that you will feel pressured within the learning environment.

When on clinic placement, mature students often find that the clients' parents or relatives often seem to forget that they are students. They do know you are a student but as you appear older they may well expect you to be more knowledgeable than you feel you are. An advantage for you in this situation is that they may feel more comfortable with you and have more confidence in you.

Chapter 31 Studying and professional development

The subjects you will study

In the main, all courses cover the same topics and theoretical learning will be integrated with practical learning although, as discussed in Part III, each course will have its own emphasis.

The main areas of study are listed below with an explanation of their relevance to the practice of speech and language therapy.

Theoretical aspects

☐ *Speech and language pathology* is the study of communication breakdown and disorder across the lifespan. It provides an understanding of what happens when there is disease or disorder in a specific part of the body that contributes to the breakdown of communication, or that prevents communication developing normally. You will learn about the nature of different disorders as well as how therapists work as members of multi-disciplinary teams to enable clients to achieve their potential.

☐ *Phonetics* is concerned with the description and analysis of the pronunciation of spoken language. The study of phonetics helps to train your ear to listen acutely so that you can recognise all aspects of your own and others' speech that you can then transcribe.

☐ *Linguistics* is the description and analysis of language. You will learn how to elicit and monitor linguistic behaviour and to understand what language patterns can tell you about communication breakdown. It includes developing an understanding of how children acquire language as well as what happens when language breaks down.

❑ *Psychology* has several aspects that are relevant to speech and language therapy. Developmental psychology is concerned with how behaviour may change at different ages and stages. Abnormal psychology is a study of mental health problems such as schizophrenia and dementia. Social psychology looks at sociological aspects including how people function in groups in work and at play, and includes non-verbal communication.

❑ *Psycholinguistics* is a way of looking at the interaction between psychological development, and language development and break down.

❑ *Research design and statistics* enable you to design your own evaluation studies and research projects and to read and understand the research of others, for example, in journal articles.

❑ *Hearing sciences* including audiology, acoustics and perception of speech and hearing help you to understand the relationship of the effects of what you hear on what you say.

❑ *Anatomy and physiology* are studied so that you can understand the structure and function of the human body, particularly in relation to communication and swallowing.

❑ *Neurology* helps you to understand the functioning of the brain and the nervous system so that you can appreciate the impact that damage will have on specific parts of the system relating to communication and swallowing.

❑ *Medical aspects* enables you to understand what can go wrong in relation to communication and swallowing disorders when the body is diseased, damaged or ceases to function appropriately.

❑ *Educational issues* include special educational needs. You will learn about the education system in the UK and how speech and language therapists work within it. You will learn about the importance of collaborating with colleagues in educational settings so that a child's speech and language therapy is integrated into classroom learning.

❐ *Multi-cultural issues* relate to developing an understanding of how exposure to an additional language might affect a child's overall speech and language development. You will also need to be aware of the possible effects of growing up in a multi-cultural household and interpersonal interactions in different cultures.

Professional development

Practical placements

One of the distinguishing features of a speech and language therapy course is that as part of your course you will carry out practical work on a placement under the supervision of a qualified therapist. You may work in a health centre, a mainstream school, a special school, or unit, a hospital, a rehabilitation centre or a day centre. During your course you will have a range of experiences although it is unlikely that you will experience all of these settings. You may work on a day-release basis and sometimes for a block of time that may be as short as a week or as long as several months.

Often you will have to travel a long way to a placement. You may be working with one or more students from your course or you may attend alone. Each clinical supervisor will have a different way of working; some will work closely with you while others prefer to leave you to work much of the time independently. However, all supervising clinicians have to put their clients' needs first.

Usually placements are supported by clinical tutorials held at the university. Often you will have theory and practical work with similar client groups running concurrently so you are learning in college about what you are seeing in clinic. However, this is not always possible and you will usually have to do additional reading for yourself to help you understand better the clients with whom you are working.

Also, during your time on the course it will not be possible for you to work with every kind of client group so that it will be important to share your experiences with other students in your year. Reading the RCSLT *Bulletin* and *Speech and Language Therapy in Practice* will help you keep up-to-date on ways in which therapists are working and make you aware of current clinical issues.

Other practical work

This will vary according to the university but most courses include tutorials, workshops and practical sessions designed to help you develop your interpersonal skills. Such sessions may include an introduction to basic counselling skills, assertiveness training, presentation skills, listening skills and other key skills you will need to work successfully as a therapist. You will usually have opportunities to become familiar with technical equipment and to become desensitised to being video- and audio-recorded.

Learning and Teaching

Each university will have its own approach to learning and teaching and each will include a variety of teaching styles. There will normally be a mix of formal lectures, seminars, practical workshops, labs, back-up classes and small group tutorials. There will be required readings and each course will have its own form of assessment, usually combining course work and examinations.

If you are interested in understanding about how adults learn you could read Chapter 2 in *Speech and Language Therapy: the decision making process* (see *Further Reading*).

Having a professional attitude

Professionalism encompasses many different aspects such as acting in a disciplined way, displaying competence and a demeanour that instils confidence in your clients and their carers. This is quite different from being in a student role. Professionalism includes not missing appointments, always being on time, managing the time during sessions, taking responsibility and showing you can work independently, showing appropriate respect for clients and colleagues, always being well prepared, working effectively as part of a team and appreciating confidentiality.

For some students this is a natural role for them to take. Others find they develop more gradually into the professional role. As a professional you will not necessarily have all the answers, although you will know where to look for the appropriate information and you will also understand the limitations of your own professional role.

Part V
Now You Are Qualified...

Chapter 32 Applying for a job

Congratulations! You have completed the course. But once the euphoria has died down you might think, now what? One of the advantages of studying to become a speech and language therapist is that you are qualified to work as a therapist as soon as you have registered with the HPC having successfully completed your course. In fact, many students apply for jobs before their final exams. At the time of writing there is still a great demand for speech and language therapists and there are many jobs available.

Registration

Whether you have already been offered a job, or you are just beginning to think about applying, anyone who wishes to practise in the UK as a speech and language therapist **must** apply for registration with the HPC before they can begin to work. Examination pass lists are sent directly to the HPC by the education establishments so they will already have your name on file pending your application. This is also the time to apply to become a qualified member of RCSLT.

The professional body RCSLT holds a register of all its members who are practising therapists as well as non-practising members, those who are now retired, and those working overseas. When students qualify their names are held on a graduate list until their managers certify that they have completed one year of satisfactory working practice. They may then apply to be transferred to the RCSLT's full practice list. The purpose of the graduate list is to ensure that newly qualified therapists get all the support they need in their first year of practice.

The job application

Whenever you are ready to apply for your first job you need to approach the form filling and the interview in the same way as you approached your application to the university. The application and interview for a first job offer you, as a newly qualified speech and language therapist, the first opportunity to market yourself.

You need to find out as much about the job as possible. Normally a job description and a person specification will be sent to you with the application form and this will outline the skills, experience, knowledge and qualities you will need for the post. If there is a number to ring for informal contact then make sure you take the opportunity to find out more about the setting in which you could be working. You can usually use the Internet to find out more about the setting and you may want to read some relevant literature about the client group.

The application form

Just like university applications, when you fill out the form make sure it's legible. It's a good idea to get someone else to proof-read it before sending it off. Always take a photocopy so that you can read it before going into the interview. It doesn't give a good impression if you have forgotten what you have said! Make sure you send it in well before the deadline.

The job interview

If you are called for interview, this is your opportunity to show that you are the one for the job. This is your chance to promote yourself and to flag up your skills, knowledge, and expertise. For example, make links between the questions asked and all your relevant personal experiences particularly relating to your clinical placements.

Your first job will usually be as a generalist speech and language therapist, as you will not have been trained for a more specialist post.

Chapter 33 Professional life after qualification

Your first job

Now that you're registered with HPC and have been successful at interview, you are ready to start your first job. Here there will be an induction period that will vary in length in different authorities. You will be given details about the specific standards of practice of your employing service such as health and safety information. You may have a specific mentor assigned to you. You will also have a line-manager who will usually offer some form of supervision as recommended in RCSLT's, *Communicating Quality*.

Normally, newly qualified therapists make the transition to full clinical autonomy in about a year. Your manager will then be ready to confirm that you are competent to be transferred to the RCSLT full practice list.

What if you want to specialise?

Newly qualified therapists are qualified to work with adults and/or children. You don't usually have a specialised role in a first job, as it is more usual for a new therapist to start by working with a mixed or generalised caseload. Most graduates have a preference for the type of clients they want to work with, or the setting in which they would prefer to work.

However, you may find yourself changing your mind. This could be influenced by the posts available, particularly if you are restricted to a geographic location, or if you wish to work for a specific authority. If you have no particular preference it may be possible to work in a rotational post where you will experience a range of client groups and settings and you can specialise later if you wish.

There are several different ways of specialising. You might gain experience 'on the job' by working with a specific client group. Or, it might be possible to increase the amount of time you spend with a particular client group. In addition, you may find other ways of increasing your specialist knowledge, for example by joining an RCSLT Special Interest Group (SIG) where therapists hold meetings and discussions, or run courses to further their knowledge in a specific area.

You may also find short courses to help you develop your knowledge and skills. These may be in-service training courses that are part of your job or courses run by other organisations. Sometimes these may lead to a diploma or lead eventually to a Master's degree.

Continuing professional development (CPD)

When you sign your professional registration forms you will be signing an agreement to continue your professional development. Similarly, when renewing your subscription to RCSLT, you will have to produce an annual CPD log that is a record of your programme of continuous professional development. This helps you monitor your own learning. Often your individual performance review at work will influence your CPD activities for the coming year. This will be based on your learning needs in relation to your job, as well as the available resources.

CPD can take different forms such as reading books and journals, attending short courses or conferences, or attending longer courses all of which will help you keep up-to-date with the latest ideas, theories, therapies and research. You may eventually be in a position to give a paper at a conference yourself.

What if you want to work overseas?

You may work overseas as a volunteer such as through VSO (for the website see *Useful Addresses*) or you may prefer to pursue the possibility of being in paid employment. This will depend on the country in which you wish to work.

Further information can be obtained from a booklet compiled by Community Therapy International a group of therapists with experience of working overseas which is available from RCSLT (see *Useful Addresses* for details). The requirements will vary between countries, and sometimes even between states, for example, in the USA. Some countries may require you to sit additional examinations or to undertake a period of continuing study. You may also be asked for a transcript from your course showing the details of the hours and subjects studied.

RCSLT also have introductory information and details on working in a range of different countries as well as up-to-date information about countries where reciprocal recognition of UK speech and language therapy qualifications exist.

What if you want to work in private practice?

It is often advisable to gain your first experience of paid employment as a therapist within the NHS. However, many people at some stage in their career will undertake private practice or may see some private patients in addition to their NHS job.

If you wish to work in the private sector you may wish to apply for a job in a private hospital, a private school, or you may wish to set up your own private practice.

For further information contact the Association of Speech and Language Therapists in Independent Practice ASLTIP (see *Useful Addresses*).

What if you want to carry out research and study for a higher degree?

You may consider continuing your studies by undertaking a further degree although it is usually better to gain some practical experience first. There may be opportunities for research as part of your job. Therapists usually chose to study further in order to increase their knowledge in a specific area, or if they wish to improve their research skills and possibly move into teaching and research.

Many speech and language therapists apply for a non-clinical Master's programme once they have qualified and it may be possible to continue with part-time studies while in employment as a therapist. Some people are able to negotiate a leave of absence so that they can undertake such a course full-time. The courses that therapists select depend on their interests and may vary from an MSc in Human Communication or Cognitive Psychology, to an MA in Linguistics or Business Administration. Employers sometimes support staff undertaking further study either by agreeing to requests for regular study days, contributing financially towards fees or trying to reduce the workload of a staff member for the time period of the course. Some therapists choose to focus on research and will register for an MPhil leading to a PhD.

Returning after a career break

Speech and language therapists who take career breaks can return to the profession. However, if they have not practised for five years or more they will need to update their skills and knowledge. In this situation a returning therapist must work for a period under supervision to demonstrate competence as a clinically autonomous practitioner to the satisfaction of his/her manager.

You as clinical supervisor

Once therapists have been working for a couple of years they are expected to offer clinical placements to students. Hopefully, after the prescribed period you will become a clinical supervisor and offer placements to one of the universities so that you can begin to work with students too.

Appendix: Photocopyable Check Lists

1. Preparation

Do I know how to get to the venue?
Have I allowed enough time?
Am I dressed comfortably and appropriately?
Have I got a pen and a piece of paper with me?
Have I got the prospectus with me?
Have I prepared a list of questions I want answered?
Have I got those questions with me?
How will I make contact with family/friends accompanying me after the interview?
Have I turned my mobile phone off before going in to the interview?

2. If you meet the students

If you are able to meet some of the current students check out:
The accommodation
The social activities
The amount of time available for these activities
The work load
The typical travel time between accommodation and university
Canteen facilities and prices

3. To check at the university

You need to make sure you know enough about each department to be able to make an informed decision if you are lucky enough to be offered a place in more than one university – because that decision will be yours alone. So check out:
Do you like the atmosphere of the place?
Could you imagine yourself studying here?

Further Reading

If you would like to read more about speech and language problems we suggest starting with some of the following books.

Books

Crystal, D. and Varley, R. (1998) 4th edition *Introduction to Language Pathology* London: Whurr Publishers

Douglas, K. (2002) *My Stroke of Luck* London: Little Brown

Glogowska, M. (2002) *Time to Talk* London: Whurr Publishers

Haddon, M. (2004) *The Curious Incident of the Dog in the Night Time* London:Vintage

Kersner M. and Wright. J.A. (Eds) (2003) 3rd edition *How to manage communication problems in young children* London: David Fulton Publishers

Kersner, M. and Wright, J.A. (Eds) (2001) *Speech and Language Therapy: The decision making process* London: David Fulton Publishers

Parr, S.; Byng, S. and Gilpin, S. with Ireland, C. (1997) *Talking about Aphasia* Berkshire: Open University Press

Peers, J. (2003) *Asparagus Dreams* London: Jessica Kingsley Publishers

Rogers, C. and Dolva, G. (1999) *Karen has Down Syndrome* London: Jessica Kingsley Publishers

Sacks, O. (1986) *The Man who Mistook his Wife for a Hat* New York: Picador

Sacks, O. (1991) *Seeing Voices* New York: Picador

Other reading

Speech and Language Therapy in Practice
http://www/sol.co.uk/s/speechmag

Royal College of Speech and Language Therapists' Bulletin

References used within the text

Kersner M. and Wright. J.A. (Eds) (2003) 3rd edition *How to manage communication problems in young children* London: David Fulton Publishers

Kersner, M. and Wright, J.A. (Eds) (2001) *Speech and Language Therapy: The decision making process* London: David Fulton Publishers

Royal College of Speech and Language Therapists (1996) *Communicating Quality 2* London: RCSLT

All counselling references relate to Carl Rogers' client-centred counselling approach.

Useful Addresses

Afasic, http://www.afasic.org.uk

ASLTIP (Association of Speech and Language Therapists in Independent Practice), http://www.helpwithtalking.com

The British Stammering Association, http://www.stammering.org

Community Therapy International, http://www.ctint.co.uk

Dept of Higher and Further Education Northern Ireland, http://www.nics.gov.uk/hfe.htm

Health Professions Council, http://www.HPC-uk.org

I CAN, http://www.ican.org.uk

Mencap, www.mencap.org.uk

NHS Student Grants Unit, http://www.nhspa.gov.uk/sgu/

RCSLT, www.rcslt.org

Scope, http://www.scope.org.uk

The Stroke Association, http://www.stroke.org.uk

Students Awards Agency for Scotland, www.student-support-saas.gov.uk

UCAS Enquiries, www.ucas.ac.uk

Voice Association http://www.british-voice-association.com

Voluntary Service Overseas www.vso.org.uk

Index

access course 72, 158, 159

accommodation 185

acquired disorders 30, 105-110

agency work 51

'A' levels 72,158

alternative and augmentative communication (AAC) 67, 138

application form 76, 81, 167, 169, 195

applying for a first job 194

assistants 8, 38, 42, 59, 94, 111, 113, 121, 138, 165, 168

bilingual (*see also* multi-cultural) 113, 146

British Sign Language (BSL) 6, 62, 94, 101, 145-8, 166

career prospects 3

cerebral palsy 24, 25, 26, 29, 101, 103, 121

classroom assistants (*see* assistants)

clinic placements (*see* placements)

cognitive 14, 24, 26, 57, 103,110, 132, 200

communication aids 125

communication difficulties/disorders 5, 20-32, 51, 72, 84, 93, 94, 160, 164, 171

continuing professional development (CPD) 80, 86, 89, 98, 138, 198

developmental disorders 30

dysphagia (*see also* eating and drinking problems) 26, 42, 101, 140

eating and drinking problems (*see also* dysphagia) 2, 12, 26, 38, 58, 101, 103, 121

examinations 78, 132, 190, 196

experience 8, 70, 72, 84, 85, 88, 94

entry requirements 77, 158, 162

first job 47, 86, 195, 196, 197

frequently asked questions 2-9

funding 5, 161-2

gap year 105, 116, 130, 170-1, 183

Health Professions Council (HPC) 12, 55, 91, 151, 153, 194, 197

highers 72, 158, 159

hospitals 8, 12, 31, 38, 44, 45, 46, 49, 50, 51, 94, 105-110, 140-144, 165, 166, 182, 189, 199

in-service training (INSET) 102, 106, 114, 147, 198
International Baccalaureate 72, 159
international students 162
interview for a first job 195
interview for university 162, 173-6, 178, 202
Irish Highers (*see* Highers)
IT skills 71, 77

language disorders (*see* communication difficulties/disorders)
learning and teaching 190
learning disabilities 6, 8, 25, 26, 27, 28, 38, 40, 43, 46, 50, 66, 84, 94, 103, 105, 135-139
learning support assistants (see assistants)
line-manager 98, 121, 133, 143, 168, 197
lifelong learning 88, 91
locum work (*see* agency work)

mainstream schools (*see* schools)
Makaton 6, 101, 102, 138
mature students 2, 7, 58, 72, 94, 158, 159, 165, 182, 183, 184, 186
multi-cultural 5, 54, 189

non-verbal communication 14, 17, 18, 27, 29, 57, 90, 136, 188
nurseries 31, 41, 47, 48, 95, 128, 165

overseas students (*see* International students)

parent-child interaction programme 41
personal statement 76, 168, 169, 175
physical disabilities/difficulties 14, 22, 24, 29, 31, 54, 62, 67, 94, 121-125, 132
placement(s) 6, 43 59, 73, 74, 76-79, 81, 82, 88, 111, 116, 151,152, 166, 170, 173, 175, 182, 184, 186, 189, 195, 201
pragmatics 18
pragmatic problems/difficulties 25, 28
private practice 45, 51, 199
professional attitude/ professionalism 33-34, 70, 191
professional body (*see* Royal College of Speech and Language Therapists)

qualities 68-85, 86-92, 164, 182, 195

references 168
registration 5, 51, 91, 151, 153, 194, 198
research 91, 188, 200
research project 6, 188

Royal College of Speech and Language Therapists (RCSLT) 6, 8, 44, 55, 93, 106, 119, 153, 162, 165, 183, 190, 194, 197, 198, 199

salary 8, 55
schools 8, 12, 31, 38, 45, 46, 47, 48-9, 84, 102, 111-115, 121-5, 126-9, 131, 145-8, 165
Scottish Highers (*see* Highers)
skills 3, 16-17, 33, 35, 39, 56, 57, 62, 68-85, 86-92, 159, 160, 164-166, 169, 170, 171, 173, 175, 178, 182, 183, 184, 186, 190, 195, 198, 200
social skills 25, 28, 125, 136
special educational needs 94, 95, 188
Statement of special educational needs 113
special interest group (SIG) 119, 128,142, 183, 198
specialisation/specialist 47, 50, 86, 88-9, 98-104, 105-110, 116-120, 140-144, 145-8, 196, 198
special schools (*see* schools)
speech disorders (*see* communication difficulties/disorders)

speech and language therapy assistants (*see* assistants)
stroke 12, 20, 22, 23, 24, 25, 26, 28, 29, 31, 34, 36, 37, 39, 42, 44, 45, 50, 66, 69, 74, 95, 105, 106, 107, 108, 109, 132, 133, 134, 166
subjects studied 57,58, 187-189,199
swallowing problems (*see* dysphagia *and* eating and drinking problems)

the therapy process 60
time management 44, 78, 173

university courses 154-7

voluntary sector /voluntary work 3, 50, 51, 84, 94, 95, 165, 177
Voluntary Service Overseas (VSO) 51, 199

work experience 5, 94, 165, 168, 169
working abroad 51, 171